Fl

AS WIDE AS
THE RIVER

AS WIDE AS THE RIVER

DH 56981

DEAN HUGHES

Deseret Book Company
Salt Lake City, Utah
1980

© 1980 Deseret Book Company
All rights reserved
Printed in the United States of America

Library of Congress Cataloging in Publication Data

Hughes, Dean, 1943-
    As wide as the river.

I. Title.
PZ4.H8922As   [PS3558.U36]   813'.54   80-14646
ISBN 0-87747-820-1

Chapter 1

"Because I told you to, Joseph. Isn't that reason enough?"

"I only thought—"

"You only thought to go against your father's will again. You only thought to do things your own way, regardless of what I say."

Joseph gave up, as he often had lately. Something had happened to his father. He seemed irritable almost all the time, and the slightest little upset could set off these outbursts. But today something beyond that, something akin to rage, seemed to be stirring just beneath the surface. Joseph had only asked to go hunting with Matthew, promising to finish his wood chopping and other chores as soon as he and Matthew returned. It was something Joseph had done before; it was hardly an act of defiance to request to do so again.

But with Father's outburst Joseph gave up the entire idea, and as Matthew left the house with the old rifle that Colonel Allen had loaned the family, Joseph began his chores. He chopped wood almost violently at first, still smarting from his father's accusations, but gradually the anger subsided to sadness—an emotion Joseph had come to feel often in recent weeks.

It was early December of 1833, and the first snows had come to western Missouri. But today the weather was mild, the thin layer of clouds emitting enough sunlight to reflect off the patches of snow in the field below the house. Joseph leaned on the long-handled ax and rested for a moment. His eyes returned, as they always seemed to do, to the stretch of willows and cottonwoods in the distance that marked the banks of the Missouri River. Beyond the river lay Jackson County—Zion—the place Joseph Smith, the Mormon prophet, had designated for the building of the city of God. The Mormons would return—Joseph had been told that many times—but would his house still be there? Had the old settlers already burned it or torn it down? He hated the old shanty he lived in now; it was cold and small and there was no wooden floor. In fact, it was really just an old shed that Father had converted into a shelter for the family. They would not be there long, Joseph had been promised, but he wondered. When would things ever start to go well again?

Joseph went back to his chopping, but in a few minutes his mother came out. "Joseph," she said, "stop for a minute. I want to talk to you." Joseph put down his ax and looked at his mother. She had wrapped a shawl around her shoulders and was holding it close to her body. She looked terribly thin and something else—maybe tired. Her hair was pulled tightly back into a bun, emphasizing the leanness of her face, and her eyes looked colorless, deep-set. "Joseph, your father is sorry; I know he is. He can't say it just yet, but I know that he would like to."

"All I said was that I—"

"I know, Joseph. You don't need to tell me. It wasn't anything you said."

"Then what is it, Mother? What's he so angry about all the time?"

"He's sick, Joseph. You know that. He has never really gotten well since those men beat him. He never should have gone back to work so soon. He almost killed himself getting this old shed into condition so we could move in. He got wet and cold too many times. It weakened him more than we realized at first."

"I know he's not well. I understand that. But he's never acted like this before. I can't say anything around him without making him angry."

"I know, Joseph." What she didn't say, but what Joseph knew, was that he was the same with all of them, even

2

with her. "We must be patient with him. Your father is frightened, Joseph. He's lost his strength and it doesn't seem to come back. He lies there on his bed and thinks about all there is to do—and all that we had and lost—and he wants to get up and do something about it. But the fever comes back every day—and you know how he tires out when he gets up and around."

"What are we going to do, Mother?"

"He'll get better. Once he can get back to work things will be fine. We'll build a house in the spring, and Colonel Allen says we can farm this land and not pay any rent until the harvest. We'll buy the land in time, Joseph. Or else we'll go back to our home across the river."

Joseph had known what she would say. It was what she always said; it was what Newel Knight said, and what Bishop Partridge said. And Joseph Smith had said the same thing in his letters from Ohio. But it was hard for Joseph to believe that he would ever have a real house again, especially that he would go back to the one his family had been forced out of in Jackson County. The Saints were so scattered now, and so many were sick; they were living in barns and sheds, even in tents. Everyone said that for now the problem was to survive the winter, that things would go better in the spring. But Joseph could hardly imagine strength arising out of so much weakness.

Joseph looked back toward the river and beyond it to where gray hills faded into the horizon. He tried to leave the thought alone, but it was never far from his consciousness: Why did it all have to happen? How could God have allowed it to happen?

"Be patient with him, Joseph. All right?"

Joseph nodded, picking up the ax.

"There's something more, Joseph." Joseph set the ax back down and looked at his mother again. "Yesterday afternoon when Colonel Allen came by he told me that Mrs. Reynolds, down the road about a mile, is down with the ague. They need someone to help out and will pay three dollars a week until she's on her feet again. I told

3

your father but he said that he would not allow it. That's why he's upset."

"I guess he'll forget it soon enough," Joseph said.

"No, he won't, Joseph. I have thought it over. I am going to take the work—at least for two or three weeks."

Joseph was surprised in a way, and yet his life had become so disoriented that surprises had become common. During the days that his father had lain sick in bed Joseph had noticed a new authority in his mother, but he had not expected her to go this far. He did not think she would go against Father's will, not defiantly.

"What he was saying to you he was really saying to me, Joseph. I think he knows what I plan to do."

"But Matthew gets work some days at the slaughter yard. Isn't that enough, Mother? And he hunts on other days. We can get by, can't we?"

"Joseph, I wish we could. I have thought all night about it. But we need everything. All that we have is either borrowed from Colonel Allen or else so worn it's almost useless. We need money. Father can build a house in the spring and we'll put in a crop, but we need dishes and bedding and furniture. Joseph, your father cannot do it all. We simply must have some cash to buy some of the things. If he works too hard, too soon again, he will die. I know he will. And Joseph, you know him; he'll kill himself working rather than give up. I have to do it; I can't see any other way."

There were no tears in her eyes; she was clear-eyed, almost angry. Joseph saw that she was taking her stand. "Will you go every day?" Joseph asked.

"Except for the Sabbath, yes. And I guess you know what that means. I will take the baby with me, but you will have to watch Ruth most of the time. Matthew will be gone most days and Father is not well enough yet to look after her. And you will have more chores here."

"I don't mind chores, Mother. And Ruth is no burden." He stopped short, not wanting to say it. "It's just that being with Father . . . "

4

"I know, Joseph. I have thought about that. But I can't think what else to do. I believe the Lord has given me a way to help us out of our condition. Joseph, look at our clothes. We can't wear them much longer. What else can I do but try to earn a little money?"

Joseph did not want to decide who was right. It didn't matter to him very much. What mattered was that the long winter would be longer than ever. He wished that he were the older brother—fourteen like Matthew—so that he could go out and work and hunt. He would soon be twelve, but he feared he would always be the one forced to do the women's chores while his brother went out and learned to be a man.

"When are you going to tell him?" Joseph said.

"I did already, Joseph. Just before I came out here. He told me that I could not do it, but I am going in the morning; I feel sure he knows. I'll leave a johnnycake and some mush for you tomorrow. You can turn the cake on the board after I go so that it will be ready when he wakes up. You can cut some salt pork for dinner and finish the johnnycake with that."

"All right. I guess we'll get by."

"Thank you, Joseph. I'm sorry it must be this way."

Joseph picked up his ax. He decided to spend the whole day outside. He would catch up on all the chores while the weather was mild. And that way he would not have to go in to face Father's black mood. There would be enough of that in days to come. But for the moment Joseph looked back toward the river. The breeze tangled his hair, which he had not bothered to comb that morning. It was hair the color of spring honey, like his mother's, and his eyes were like his mother's too—blue in their season, but now colorless and full of worry.

For the next two weeks Mother got up early every morning and walked to the Reynolds place. It snowed after a few days and the weather turned fairly cold, but she bundled Samuel up and wore Father's old blanket coat over her shoulders, wrapping it around herself and the baby. At

5

night she had to sit by the fire and thaw out her feet. Her only shoes were buckskin moccasins that she had made herself. She returned after dark each night looking tired and worn, but she immediately set about preparing supper. Joseph knew that she was having trouble providing enough milk for the baby. Samuel was cross and often cried at night. Mother mentioned one day that she was giving him a little cow's milk sometimes and that it didn't sit well on his stomach.

Through all this Father said very little. Joseph had expected a storm, but it had never come. Though Father was sullen and cranky, not once did he even mention to Joseph where Mother was going each day, and she never mentioned it either. Joseph knew that what his father was experiencing was shame. But instead of fighting back, he seemed to have given up for the present. He slept half the day and rarely tried to rise from his bed. Joseph offered to help him dress and walk a bit, but Father only shook his head, staring at the fire or at the clapboards of the ceiling. And he ate far too little.

Joseph found his days tedious. He would go outside to chop wood for a while each day, even when the weather was severe, but he dared not be outside too long. Ruth, who was five, was a fairly independent little girl who could play with her moth-eaten rag doll for hours, but she had little understanding of her father's moods. If she tired of playing she often demanded that Joseph tell her stories. She was just as likely to make the same demands on Father. Joseph knew that Father tried hard to be patient with Ruth, but he also feared that she might annoy him, which would only make things worse.

Just keeping the little cabin warm was full-time work. Father had added a stick-and-mortar fireplace to the old shed, but it was inefficient, sucking most of the heat up the chimney. And the logs in the walls were not as well chinked as they needed to be. The cold air blew in so badly when it was windy outside that the only warm place was directly in front of the fire. Joseph tried to keep the fire as large as possible.

One morning in Mother's third week of working, the snow set in very hard. Mother cut some bacon that Matthew had been able to bring home from the slaughter yard and started a johnnycake on the board by the fire. Father had begun to get up a bit more in recent days. That morning he got up and took a look outside. It was the first time he had gotten up before Mother had left in the morning. But apparently he had heard the force of the wind and wanted to see what the weather was like.

"Elizabeth," he said, as he shut the door, "you can't go today. The snow is getting deep and the wind is drifting until you won't be able to see the road."

"Matthew, I don't see how I can do that. Mrs Reynolds needs me. She's not at all well."

Joseph saw his father bring himself up, his legs set firm and his chest expanded. The silent submission was about to end. Mother turned from the fire and looked at her husband. She saw it too, and she faced him.

"Mrs. Reynolds will have to find another *domestic*," he said. "Let them buy themselves a slave, since they're Virginia people anyway. You are *not* going back there."

"Matthew, I can't just quit without a word. I must at least go back until they can find someone else."

"I'll go over and tell them just as soon as this weather breaks. And I'll take with me that slab of beef they sent home with you last night. I'll not take handouts."

"Handouts!" Mother's voice was suddenly high-pitched; Joseph knew that she was angry. "Matthew, I have worked very hard. Mrs. Reynolds gave me the meat because she said I earned it by my diligence. She said her house had never been in better order."

"Then it is time to get ours in order, Elizabeth."

"I've kept things in—"

"That's not what I mean, Elizabeth, and you know it. I am the man of this house and I *will* be respected. You go off each day and leave me here like a woman with the children. I'll have no more of it. I am going to work myself." He turned to his son, young Matthew, who had just gotten out of bed and pulled on his breeches. "Matthew, is there work for men at the slaughter yard?"

"Yes, Father, but it's heavy."

"Good. Then I'll walk over this afternoon if the snow lets up at all, and I'll see whether I can't get work."

"You are not ready," Mother said. "You can't go out in this cold. You know that you will be right back in bed."

"No, I won't, Elizabeth. I'm not going back to bed." He stood staring at his wife for a moment, his breath coming with apparent difficulty. And then, as though he felt his own weakness coming over him, he added, "I may not be able to work hard yet, but I will soon. I'm getting better. But for right now, I want you to quit. I will sit here no longer while you make a slave of yourself to those people."

"Oh, Matthew, how can you say such a thing? I'm no slave. And the Reynoldses are fine people, good Christians. They welcome the Saints and are happy to help us if they can."

"Well, I do not welcome their help. You give them time and you will find they are the same kind of heathens that we met in Jackson County. It's just a matter of time until it all starts again."

"That isn't fair, Matthew. You've never met them. How can you say such things?"

"The point is, Elizabeth, you are not going back there any more."

"All right, Matthew. I won't go back today. But I must go back for at least a few days after the storm—until they can get someone else, and until you are ready to work."

Joseph watched his father step toward his mother and grasp her shoulder. For a moment Joseph thought that he would strike her. But all Father's strength was thrown into his voice, which thundered: "Everyone in this household has forgotten who I am." He took a few long, steady breaths as the firelight glinted off his eyes and the glossi-

8

ness of his black beard. Joseph could see that Father was beginning to tire.

Mother's voice was subdued when she said, "No, Matthew, we have not. But you are sick. We must do what is necessary for now. I felt that I could not pass up this chance—that is all. We have no furniture, Matthew, no . . . anything. We need seed in the spring, and we need a plow and tools. And a cow. I don't have . . ." Her voice tightened and she swallowed. Joseph could see the tears come to her eyes. "Matthew, I don't have enough milk for Samuel. If I don't go to the Reynoldses' he may not live. Have you looked at him? He's thin, Matthew, and he's had the colic for weeks. You haven't known. You've had to rest. But I had to find a way. I had to do what I have done, Matthew."

Father's grip on his wife's shoulder lightened; he looked into her face for some time and then patted her two or three times. It was the most affection he had shown her in weeks. "Elizabeth, they took everything from us. If I just had the strength of my two hands, I could do something. I could try to get everything back. It's *that* that I hate them for. They robbed me of even my power to work." He sounded changed, humbled, and yet bitterness clung to his words. Joseph had never seen his father so broken. "I'll build you a new house, Elizabeth, and we'll have cows and oxen and horses. We'll have a good farm again yet. I'll give you all you deserve if the Lord will just give back my strength."

"I know you will, Matthew, I know you will. But rest now and I will stay home with you today. I'll only go back to the Reynoldses' until we can find another way."

"What about the baby?"

"Maybe the rest will help me too. Maybe I'll have more milk if I eat some good meat and relax for a day."

Father stood before Mother for another few moments. Joseph could see his eyes twitch and his hands quiver. Then Father looked at Ruth and Matthew and Joseph, who had gathered by the fire. He seemed to want to say

9

something but finally did not. He went over to the wooden box that Samuel slept in, leaned over and lifted up the blankets, and looked at his son. He lingered there for some time before tucking the blankets back; then he went to his own bed and sat down. He stared straight ahead for a time and then put his hands over his face, resting his elbows on his knees. No one moved; everyone watched him. Joseph did not know whether Father was crying or not, but he knew that Mother was. Eventually Father lay down and in a few minutes fell asleep. He slept almost all morning.

Chapter 2

Father did seem to be regaining some of his strength during the next few days. But he was plagued with a constant cough that rumbled from deep within him. It made sleeping difficult not only for him but for the whole family, since the beds were all so close in the little room. Samuel was not doing very well either. He had apparently caught cold, and it was difficult for him to breathe at times. At night he often cried a sort of listless whimper with no real energy behind it. Joseph worried also about his mother, who was looking very worn. Every day she trudged through the snow to the Reynolds farm. Fortunately, the storm had abated before the snow had become deep, but when the clouds had cleared away the temperatures had dropped very low. Joseph carried water from the spring every morning, but now he had to break through thick ice to get to the water, and he had to set the bucket close to the fire or the water would freeze inside the house.

Joseph hated to see the way his mother looked. She had repaired her old linsey-woolsey dress many times; it was the one she had worn on the day she had been forced from her home in Jackson County. She had another dress, a calico that Mrs. Reynolds had given her, but she saved it for best, for the days when she was able to go to church. Both dresses hung on her loosely now that she was so thin. She seemed to have lost all her softness and was starting to look like the old settlers' women, all bone and sinew.

On Sundays some of the Saints from the old Colesville settlement assembled for church services at Newel Knight's log cabin, which was among the bluffs north of the river a little more than three miles from where Joseph and his family were living. In time the Colesville Saints planned to build a church; they wanted to stay together as much as possible. Joseph and Matthew went to the services most Sundays, but since the weather had turned cold they had stopped going to the Wednesday evening meetings. Father, of course, was not able to go, so Mother usually stayed with him and the two smaller children. But when the boys returned, Mother quizzed them for every detail of what had happened. She wanted to know who had given the sermons, what they had said, what the Saints' plans were. Matthew never seemed to tire of relating all that he had heard. Joseph would say, "Brother Newel talked and he said that we all ought to live the commandments. He said if we had lived them the way we should have, back in Jackson, we would never have been driven out." But Matthew would fill in the details, remembering even what hymns had been sung, which of the sisters had sent greetings, which of the people were down with the fever, and which had received letters from the East.

Father listened to all this with apparent interest, and yet with the same sullen carelessness. He asked no questions himself, and he never expressed any desire to assemble with the Saints.

Christmas was approaching now, but Joseph tried not to think about it. He knew there would be no gifts, no fine dinners, no parties. He told his mother that he didn't mind, and he really did not mind all that much, but he was more comfortable if he just avoided thinking about it. The fine Christmas celebrations back in New York were far away and gone now, and pleasant times in the Jackson County settlement had to be pushed back into the past in the same way.

When Christmas Eve did come, however, Joseph was feeling rather gloomy, and it was not hard to see that the whole family felt the same way. Joseph had been longing to go visit the Peck boys, but he dared not even mention the idea to Father. Mother had brought home some packages from the Reynoldses and so he knew that he would have some small gift, but it was hardly a celebration, especially with Father so quiet and unhappy. Late in the day, however, Newel Knight, the president of the Colesville Branch, did pay a visit. Joseph was overjoyed for the break in the quiet monotony.

Brother Newel had aged a great deal in the last few months and Joseph noticed it every time he saw him. Nonetheless, he looked ruddy and strong as he came in from the cold, stomping his feet and shaking his old blanket coat with the holes worn in the elbows. His old pantaloons were patched in the knees and worn almost threadbare, and his boots were pulling apart in the seams. What a change from the proud young Easterner in a fine suit of clothes who had first come to these western parts! But he looked happy, and Joseph was glad to see a happy face.

"How are you all?" he wanted to know. "How are you doing, Sister Williams?"

"We're coming along fine," Mother answered. "Isn't Matthew looking stronger?"

"Yes, indeed. Glad to see you up, Brother Williams; how are you feeling?"

"Much better," Father said, and he stood up finally, but he shook hands rather limply.

"Now, Matthew, what's that for a handshake? I know that strong grip of yours."

"I am afraid my grip is mostly gone, Brother Knight. I can't seem to rid myself of this fever." Father sat down on his bed again.

Brother Knight greeted the children and shook their hands. He asked about the baby, and he asked young Matthew how his leg was healing. Matthew told him that the wound hardly troubled him at all any more. Then Brother Knight turned his attention back to Father. "Now, Matthew, you be patient." He put his hand on Father's shoulder. "You have been through plenty. You can count yourself fortunate to be as far along as you are. Give yourself another month or two and you will be all the man you

13

have ever been. Half the settlement is sick, brother, and some are not coming back from it as quickly as you are."

"I suppose," was all that Father would say.

"You get strong, Matthew," Brother Knight said. "We're going to need you when we start back to Zion to retake our homes."

"Brother Knight," Mother asked, "is that really possible? Here, let me take your coat. Sit down by the fire and tell us what is happening."

Brother Knight kept his coat, saying he would have to be leaving before long, but he did take a stool and sit by the fire. "Well, we heard from Joseph Smith. He says not to sell our Jackson lands and to do our best here in Clay County for now. Governor Dunklin has written us, and he says that the old settlers were clearly in the wrong to drive us out and to take our weapons. He promises to help us go back. He wants to hold some hearings, and he promises to raise a militia to help us go back to our homes—the ones that they didn't burn."

"But won't there be bloodshed?" Mother asked. "Is it worth it?" She was sitting on the other old stool, also near the fire. Joseph and Matthew were standing near her, while Ruth had sidled up to Brother Knight. She seemed to long for closeness. Brother Knight put his arm around her shoulders and pulled her up next to him.

"Well, Sister Williams, I still feel the Lord will help us to return sooner or later, and so there must be a way. We need the courts on our side. Judge Ryland has promised a fair hearing, and I think he is a good man. He says that he wants to help us. He has already said that we are in the right. So maybe in the spring things will look better for us. But we have managed pretty well, considering everything, haven't we?"

Joseph knew this was all meant to cheer them up. He knew that things were really not going very well for many of the Saints. But he enjoyed hearing Brother Knight anyway. Father continued to sit away from the rest, still on his bed, still staring off in the distance. "Matthew, you

14

seem discouraged," Brother Knight said. "Is there some way I can help?"

"No," Father said, rather too tensely. "I don't mean to sound ungrateful, Brother Newel, but I don't like all this help I have been forced to take. Colonel Allen has loaned us everything we have—and now Elizabeth is off doing day labor for the Reynoldses. I don't like it. All I ask is that the Lord return some of my strength so that I can do for myself."

"Well now, brother, don't you fret yourself. If someone else were down and you were up, you would be the first to give help. And I wouldn't concern yourself about Sister Williams taking work for a while. Many of our women have been forced to take on jobs. In the winter they can get work more easily than the men can. We can't trouble ourselves about that right now; for the present we have to get by however we can. In the spring there will be work for all of us. And most of us will be able to rent land to work, maybe even buy some. If we go back into Jackson—"

"Brother Knight," Father said, "if I have to die for the sake of Zion I will do just that—if that's what the Prophet says to do. But I am getting tired of all this pretense. You know as well as I do that we will not just walk back to our farms while the old settlers sit by and watch, courts or no courts."

This was something Joseph did not like to think about, especially on Christmas Eve, but it was something he had often wondered about himself. He wanted no part of going back to his old home if it meant more fighting, more houses being torn down, more living in daily fear. But Joseph was embarrassed for Father. It was inappropriate to talk this way to Brother Knight, who had obviously come to bring what encouragement he could.

"Well, we'll see, Matthew. We'll see what happens. But I know we can trust the Lord. It might be that we will still have to suffer plenty before the blessings come, but I know that the Lord will bless his people—the ones who suffer for his sake and never lose the faith. Maybe we are supposed to go back to Zion now and build the city of God, and maybe we should stay here in Clay County and wait for the day to come. But whatever it is that we are supposed to do, I am sure that the Lord will prepare the way."

"All I ask is the strength to do my part."

"It's a worthy thing to ask, Brother Williams. But we have to trust in God's wisdom, and all things must come in their own due time."

To Joseph this seemed a weak answer. It was the one he had heard so often. Joseph wanted God to act now. Why wouldn't he smite the old settlers for their wickedness? And yet Joseph trusted Newel Knight and wanted to accept his forthright faith. Joseph had a difficult enough time as it was without Father's raising questions about the Lord's ways.

Brother Knight had brought some venison as a gift. He had left it outside, but now he went out and brought it in. It was his surprise for the family, to cheer them on Christmas Eve. He told them that he knew they would not be able to gather with the Colesville Saints the next day, and so he wanted them to have something that would help them enjoy Christmas.

Mother thanked Brother Knight warmly. She asked about Sally, his wife, who had also been down with the fever, and she sent her greetings to all the Saints in the Colesville Branch. Father seemed to try his best to show his appreciation. He gave Brother Knight a better handshake, but he only said, "Thank you for coming over, Brother Newel."

"Now that's better, Matthew. That's not a bad grip at all. Part of that strength you want is in your hope and faith. You can feel it coming back already, can't you?"

Father did not answer, but he nodded, if only slightly.

Christmas day was not exciting, but the dinner was the best the Williamses had had in a long time. The Reynoldses had sent home some sweet potatoes and apples. Mother baked the apples by the fire, sprinkling a little sugar over them, just as she had often done in their Jackson

County home. And Joseph thought the venison tasted wonderful. After dinner the family sang some hymns together and young Matthew read the Christmas story from Luke. Joseph and Matthew had made a checkerboard by marking squares on the crate they used for a table, and they had found some dark and light stones for pieces. They sometimes played in the evening, but today they got Father and Mother to play, and even Ruth tried to learn. Ruth really did not remember Christmas from previous years; she was so thrilled by the apples and by the little · doll cradle that the Reynoldses had sent her that her happiness affected everyone.

That evening Mother got out some hickory nuts and black walnuts she had collected in the autumn and saved for Christmas. The boys cracked them with a stone and passed them around to everyone. Samuel was still not looking very strong, but at least his cough was getting better and he was sleeping better at night. And so it was a good day, not nearly as bad as Joseph had expected. Colonel Allen had dropped by the Reynoldses that week and had given Mother two penknives, one for Matthew and one for Joseph. It was more than Joseph had ever hoped for.

Before bedtime Joseph said that he thought he would walk down to the spring and bring some water in, so that he wouldn't have to go out early in the morning. He asked Matthew if he wanted to go along and Matthew said he did.

As the boys walked outside into the cold, they both glanced up. Joseph watched his breath veil the rising moon in silver air. It was a pretty night, but so cold that Joseph's nostrils stuck shut for a moment when he took a deep breath. The boys walked side by side toward the spring.

"Listen, Matthew," Joseph said, "I want to talk to you about something. I've been thinking about it for the last few days. I have an idea—something we could do that would maybe help Father."

"What?" There was a hint of skepticism in Matthew's

17

tone, and Joseph knew that, as always, Matthew would hesitate to enter into one of Joseph's plans.

"I think I know a way we could save Mother from having to work so hard, and maybe make Father feel better at the same time."

"Joseph, I work every day that I can at the—"

"No, I don't mean anything like that."

"Then what?"

"Just hear me out, Matthew. Don't make up your mind until you hear what I have to say." Joseph let his breath puff out and watched it glide away like smoke. Why did he bother? He knew what Matthew would say. "Well, I've been thinking about all the things we left at home in Jackson County. I think we—"

"Joseph, don't even give that a second thought."

"Now, wait a minute. Just listen to me. I figure that things have calmed down a whole lot over there. We could cross on Colonel Allen's ferry. I know he would let us, and maybe he would even loan us a wagon. We wouldn't go into Independence. We would cross the Big Blue up by the mouth and then take the north road to our settlement. No one would even pay any attention to us, I'm sure. We might be able to get some of our things—like maybe some furniture—and then we wouldn't have to buy so much, or make it over again. Just think if Mother's spinning wheel and loom are still over there."

"Joseph, what are you talking about? Do you really think those things are still sitting over there? Father packed them and put them on the wagon before those men made us leave—you know that. You know those old settlers wouldn't just leave all that kind of thing sitting out in the open."

"But how do we know if we don't go back and at least take a look? Maybe some things were left, maybe lots of things. It just makes me sick to think of everything we left behind. Every day I think about the good ax we left back there. That old thing the Reynoldses gave us is almost—"

18

"*Joseph.*" Matthew stopped. Joseph walked on a little way, and then he turned around.

"What?"

"That ax is long gone, and you know it. How can you talk such nonsense?"

Joseph started to walk again, and the old bucket he was carrying squeaked as it rocked with each step. They were almost to the spring. "Maybe it's nonsense and maybe it isn't, Matthew. I have been thinking about it all the time lately. Washington Peck told me at church last Sunday that some of the brothers have been sneaking back, and they have found some things. Some found corn still in the cribs, and some got things out of their houses."

"That's fine, Joseph. But, in the first place, that was a while back—I heard about it, the same as you did. And in the second place, some got themselves beaten up. And some found their houses torn down and mostly carried off or burned right to the ground. If certain men over there recognized you or me they just might kill us, Joseph. You know that's true. You know how they feel about what I did to Mr. Brandt."

"But the thing is, Matthew, now that things have calmed down, maybe it would be easier. And maybe some of our things are still there and will be until spring. People don't get around so much in the winter."

"Joseph, it wasn't that long ago that they drove out the Saints who tried to stay on at the Prairie Settlement. Those old settlers aren't going to calm down as fast as you think."

"That was almost a month ago."

"Three weeks, maybe."

"Oh, Matthew, wouldn't it be worth a try? I look down at that river every day and I think maybe all our things are just sitting there. And we don't even try to go get them." Joseph reached down and broke the ice with his bucket, then filled it with the moonlit water that bubbled over the gray ice.

"We have our lives, Joseph, and when we got out with

19

them we were happy and thanked God. I don't think anything is left at our house, and it is just not worth taking the chance to find out. Father would never—"

"Father would never have to know. We could tell him we were going hunting early one morning. We could go over there and back in one day."

Matthew took a long look at Joseph. Joseph could see that a speech was coming. "Haven't you learned anything, Joseph? Can't you learn from the mistakes you have already made? It's always going off on your own like that, and telling lies, that gets you into trouble."

"I got *you* out of Jackson by myself, didn't I?"

"Not quite, Joseph. Not quite. Don't forget that you weren't quite alone."

Joseph had only spoken out of frustration; he knew he was wrong. But he hated Matthew's moralizing. "All right. I mean . . . I know what you are saying. But I just meant that we wouldn't have to worry Father."

"I think that if we couldn't tell him, we have a pretty sure sign that it's the wrong thing to do."

There it was: Matthew's wisdom, his great strength. Joseph admired it in a way, but he didn't like it. Matthew was always good, knew the right thing to do in every circumstance.

They started back, and for a while the boys said nothing. Matthew took the bucket from Joseph and the two walked side by side, Joseph regretting that he had ever brought up the whole idea. "Joseph, I want you to give me a promise. I want you to promise me that you won't try something like this on your own." Joseph did not answer. "Do you promise?"

"I don't see why you are so scared, Matthew."

Matthew stopped again and waited for Joseph to turn toward him. Joseph braced himself for another one of Matthew's little speeches. "I'm not scared and you know it, Joseph. If we go back—all the Saints—I'll fight if I have to. You know I will. I fought before when it came to helping Father. But I won't just run off on my own and take a big

20

chance for nothing. Now promise me that you won't either."

Joseph stared at his brother, saw his father's features hauntingly suggested in Matthew's dark eyes and solid jaw. "I don't have to promise anything, Matthew."

"I didn't say that you had to. I asked you if you would. Will you promise me?"

Joseph took a deep breath and let it flow like smoke from the stacks on the Missouri riverboats. He was no longer planning to go—it was just that he hated to let Matthew extract a promise. He hated the authority that it seemed to give to his older brother. But finally he said, "All right. I promise."

"Promise what?"

"You know what."

"Say it."

"I promise not to go off on my own and go back across the river to our old home."

"That's good," Matthew said, and they walked back to the house.

Joseph was watching the moon and the stars that were embedded in the vast blackness above. Why did everything seem so untouchable, so beyond Joseph's control? Why couldn't he have the power to alter something once in a while, especially the things that were so obviously unfair? He wanted to fight back, and just once he wanted to win.

Chapter 3

During the following weeks Father's recovery accelerated. He was certainly not the powerful man he had once been, but he was still young, not yet forty, and he began to believe he would yet regain the strength that had always sustained him. With the return of his strength came at least a partial return of optimism, and even of his old manner. Yet Joseph noticed a certain reserve about him that had not been there before the beating and the illness that had followed. He seemed suspicious and quick to condemn people's behavior, even that of the brethren in the Church. But what was almost frightening was the smoldering bitterness he still felt toward the old settlers of Jackson County.

Fortunately, the winter was not overly harsh, and spring broke rather early. As soon as the fields were dry enough, the brethren in the Colesville settlement and in all the Mormon settlements began to help each other get started plowing. They shared the teams and plows—what few they could acquire—and men went from one farm to another, getting the ground ready to plant. Some had rented farms, promising to pay at harvesttime; others worked for local farmers. Many of the Saints, both men and women, worked in the rope factory near the Missouri River. They strung long lines of hemp across elevated racks. "Human spiders" was the nickname for these workers, and it was terribly unpleasant labor, but the Mormons took what jobs they could get and began to pull themselves back to their feet. Fortunately, there was plenty of work around Liberty. Fort Leavenworth, not far away, looked to Liberty as a source of supplies, and gradually

Liberty Landing was becoming a major riverboat stop. Liberty was considerably bigger than Independence, across the river, and it was growing rapidly.

But the winter had taken its toll. Several of the Saints, especially infants, had died, and many more were severely weakened by illness. Sometimes two and three families had crowded into a single shed or converted stable. Several families had lived together in a large house that Lyman Wight had managed to rent. The tension of illness and overcrowded conditions had left people discouraged, sometimes even bitter.

In the Colesville Branch church meetings were still held at Newel Knight's place, but services were usually held outside when the weather permitted. Many more members gathered now that most were recovering from illnesses. The Williamses now walked over to the meetings together. Joseph still did not like to hear sermons preached, but he enjoyed the feeling that everyone's lot was beginning to improve. He also enjoyed seeing the Peck boys and all the Knights. He often felt lonely at his own farm, but among his Colesville friends he felt that he was with people who cared about him and his family, and who could be called upon should help ever be needed. He liked to hear the talk of plans to cooperate in raising cabins, to get everyone out of sheds and barns before very long.

One Sunday in April Brother Knight requested that everyone remain after the church services; he had important news from the Prophet in Kirtland, Ohio. After the closing prayer all remained seated on the logs that had been arranged in rows in a wide arc. Newel Knight stood again, his back to the woods. The afternoon sun was bright in his eyes, and he shaded them with his hand as he spoke.

"Brothers and Sisters, we were all happy to have Bishop Partridge with us today, and Brother John Corrill. I, for one, have been happy to have them living not far off this winter. They have been a source of much strength to us. Bishop Partridge has some news from Joseph Smith. I think you will all be interested to hear what the bishop has to say."

Bishop Partridge walked to the front. Joseph felt sad to see him in such a tattered old suit, but he was still lean and strong looking. He had always been a serious man, but now Joseph noticed something closer to sadness in his eyes. "As you know," he began, "we have received a number of letters from Brother Joseph and our other leaders in Ohio. Our instructions have not changed: we should not sell our lands; we should use the authority of the law to seek justice. What you also know is that Governor Dunklin has encouraged us to raise a little army. He says that he will give us militia support to return to our homes, but we will have to protect ourselves from then on. That, of course, we could not easily do, as we found out before. He does promise to get our arms back from the Jackson mob, but we certainly do not have enough men to fight their numbers. We have all heard rumors that the Ohio Saints might send us help. Well, that is my news. I have received word that Joseph Smith himself is coming, and that he will lead an army of at least one hundred men—five hundred, if he can raise that many—and they will come with the purpose of returning us to our lands in Jackson County."

There was an immediate stir of excitement. Joseph glanced around to see the elation on many of the faces. But he also noticed that his father looked grim.

One of the brethren said, "Bishop Partridge, will this mean war, do you suppose?"

"Well, brother, I hope not. If the Governor will send troops to take us back, as he has promised, and we have armed troops to protect us, I suspect the old settlers will finally concede."

Then Joseph saw his father stand up. "Bishop, I think we should be honest with ourselves and face this thing," he said. "Of course it will mean war." Father had not spoken bitterly, not as he had to Newel Knight earlier, on Christmas Eve, but it was not the sort of challenge to a leader that the Saints expected.

24

Everyone quieted. Bishop Partridge shaded his eyes with one hand. "No, Brother Williams, we don't know that it will come to that. We hope it won't, of course."

"Bishop, I don't think anything has changed across the river. Look what happened to Brother Miller and the other old families that tried to stay in the county. They drove them out at Christmastime—drove them like animals."

"I know that, Matthew. But I think things have begun to cool off now. Maybe—"

"Cool off? What about what happened when you tried to go back for hearings? The judge didn't even dare convene the court. Or what about Ira Willes? All he did was try to go back for his cow. Look what old Moses Wilson did to him. I don't see him at church yet, so he can't speak for himself, but I would wager that Ira would tell us those lash marks on his back are not cool at all."

"Now wait a minute, brother. I know all that. I saw Ira yesterday, and he is still mighty sore. But it has always been a few men like Wilson who got the rest stirred up. I still believe that most of the old settlers in Jackson County are decent people and would not mind living by us. It was only ten percent or so—maybe twenty—who hardened themselves so much against us."

Father would not back down. Joseph was looking at the dirt, humiliated that his father would think to argue with the bishop in front of all the members of the branch. "Ten or twenty percent of them is more than enough. They're locked in Satan's grip. They have no sense of common decency."

Bishop Partridge stood silent for a moment. He ran his hand across his balding head, pushing back the thin hair that was blowing in the breeze. He had always been a slender man, but now his face looked drawn, almost skeletal. "Well, let's not paint the picture blacker than it is," he finally said.

"Paint it blacker than it is? Bishop, I have been trying all winter to come back from the beating those devils gave me. What do you expect me to—"

25

Suddenly Newel Knight's voice broke in, not harsh but firm. "Brother Williams, we have all suffered. Bishop Partridge was humiliated—tarred and feathered and beaten. He's lived all winter with his own family and Brother Corrill's as well, fifteen of them, in an old stable. But hatred is not his way, and hatred will not help any of us. Not one of us feels any love for some of those men who caused all the trouble. But if we go back we will have to take a spirit of love and friendship with us. We'll need to win friends among the people who do *not* hate us, but we will also have to make friends of those who *do*. Nothing will destroy us faster than hatred and bitterness. There was too much of that before—too much grumbling, for one thing. I think it's why the Lord didn't protect us from the mob. It's why we lost our place in Zion."

"Amen," some of the brethren said.

Brother Williams seemed somewhat chastened, but he was still not quite ready to give up his point. "Brother Newel, I don't disagree with anything you have said. And, bishop, I surely did not mean to say that I am the only one that has suffered. But I do say that we can expect a battle if we try to go back across the river, and I think we might as well be ready for it."

"I am afraid you might be right," the bishop said, his eyes steady and solemn. He looked as firm as a statue to Joseph, but at the same time his voice imparted a sense of the man's tenderness. Joseph thought of his calm acceptance on the day the mob had covered him with tar and feathers. "Now listen, brothers and sisters," the bishop went on, "we have written to the President of the United States and other important government officials. We have hired Mr. Doniphan and Mr. Atchison again, and they are the best lawyers in these parts. I know we have spent a long winter wondering why we had to be driven out of our homes. All I know is that God has not forsaken us. We will work through legal means, and if we are supposed to go back to Zion, then God will provide a way."

But Joseph also knew that some of the Saints' leaders

had gone back to Independence for a hearing, as Father had mentioned, and the judge had sent them back because violence would have been inevitable had they stayed. The law seemed helpless against such power. It always sounded good to say that the Lord would provide a way, but Joseph had heard that back in Jackson, before the power of the mob had proven to be more powerful than anything the Mormons could raise. All the same, Joseph wanted to believe that Bishop Partridge was right; surely things had to start going better soon.

After the meeting the Williamses began the long walk home. There was next to no talk. Mother made some small attempts at conversation, commenting on the weather, wondering when the redbuds and dogwoods would begin to blossom, but Father only answered in monosyllables.

As the family approached the house, Joseph saw someone standing out front, his hands in his pockets and an old felt hat flopping across his face. He had on a rather worn-looking mackinaw jacket, of the type that riverboat men usually wore. The sun was in the man's eyes. He glanced up occasionally but then dropped his head again to allow the brim of his hat to shade his face. Joseph began to catch something familiar in the angle of the head, the unassuming stance. Then the face came up again and Joseph gasped, "Ollie."

In a moment Joseph was running toward him, yelling, "Ollie, Ollie." But Ollie stood his ground, his hands still in his pockets. Joseph would have hugged him, but Ollie took a step back and put out his hand.

"Howdy, Joseph. How are you?"

"Fine, Ollie, fine. How are *you?* How did you get here? Where have you been?"

Before Ollie could explain, Matthew walked up and extended his hand. It was an important moment and Joseph knew it. He stepped back. The two shook hands, and for just a second they looked in each other's eyes.

"Looks like you come out all right, Matthew. How's the leg?"

"It's fine, Ollie. It healed up fine. You saved my life."

Ollie did not say anything. He glanced back at Joseph.

"Where did you go, Ollie?" Joseph asked. "How did you find us?"

"Well, I went to St. Louis after I seen you last. I worked over there in the winter. Then I got me a job on a steamer and we put in over here at Liberty Landing just last night. Something's blowed up in our engine, and we's laid up here for least a few days."

Ollie had grown: he was a man as far as Joseph could tell. He had long sideburns and a healthy growth of whiskers on his chin. He seemed a little more confident, too; he talked with more ease than he ever had before.

Father and Mother had stood back, but now Mother said, "Ollie, we want to thank you for what you did to save our boys. We owe you a great deal." She came forward and shook Ollie's hand.

Father stepped forward, shifted Samuel to his other arm, and shook Ollie's hand. "I hope you will stay for supper," he said, "and you are welcome to stay the night." But Joseph felt the reserve in Father's voice. He had said the right thing, but he hardly seemed to mean it.

"I 'preciate that, sir. But I cain't stay long. I'm 'sposed to get back for night watch on the old boat tonight."

"How did you find us, Ollie?" Joseph asked again.

"On the river, lots of folks talk about how the Mormons mostly got run into Clay County, around Liberty. So when I got in to the landing here I asked if anybody knowed some Williamses. We was over at Colonel Allen's landing, and the Colonel heard me asking and said he knowed where you was, and told me how to find you."

"And so you wanted to see us again?"

"Well, I always wondered how you come out."

"We had some trouble, Ollie, but we got out finally. I'll tell you all about it. I've got lots to tell you. But we made it out, thanks to you, and now we might be going back soon. Joseph Smith is coming with—"

28

"Joseph!" Father almost shouted. "That's enough."

Ollie looked over at Father. "Sir, I sure hope none of you is thinking about trying to go back into Jackson. From what I been hearing on the river, that'd be a big mistake. Folks is mighty worked up still, and lots think Clay County folks is all wrong to take you in. They say you gotta be run clear out o' the state."

"Well, we'll see about that," Father said. "Your father and his kind may never . . . never mind." He went in the house.

Mother took hold of Ollie's arm. "Ollie, I'm sorry. Don't pay any attention. He didn't mean any harm."

Ollie nodded. "Sure. I understand. I know what my pa and them others done to him."

Ollie stayed for supper and answered Joseph's questions about St. Louis and about working on the river. To Joseph, Ollie was all the more a hero because he was a riverman. Joseph had long thought that he would like to be a riverboat pilot. Once that spring he had been allowed to walk over to the landing and watch a boat dock, and he had often watched the boats go by from the riverbank below the farm. When the boats came up the river and were about to land, a cannon was fired off that could be heard for miles. People from Liberty and all over the southern part of the county would hurry to the landing to be there for the excitement. Joseph had only gone that one time, but he had been thinking ever since how much he would like to work on the river.

After dinner Joseph asked whether he could walk back part of the way with Ollie. "Only down to the fork in the road," Father said. "It's dark outside and I don't want you going off too far."

And so Joseph walked down as far as the fork in the road. Along the way he asked Ollie more about the river and the steamer, and he told more about the escape from Jackson County. When they reached the spot where Joseph had to stop, they stood and talked a bit longer. Ollie said,

"Looks as though you folks had to leave most everything behind. Couldn't no one ever go back and get some of your things out of your house?"

"We haven't dared, Ollie. Some went back and got beaten up again. But some others did manage to bring some things out. I wanted to go, but Matthew said it wasn't worth the chance."

"Maybe I could go over and take a look around for you. No one would bother me."

"Matthew said everything would be gone."

"I 'spect he's right. But it wouldn't do no harm to have a look. I got some extra days with mighty little to do."

"Maybe Colonel Allen would let us take a' wagon, Ollie. Maybe I could go with you."

"You best not."

"Why not?"

"They might know you over there."

"No, they wouldn't, Ollie. Especially with you. We could just say we lived over there somewhere, if anybody asked."

"Well, I don't know. Maybe. Why don't you come over to the landing day after tomorrow, real early, and if we think we can do it we'll give 'er a try. Let me think on it some."

"All right. I'll come somehow. I'm not sure what I'll tell Father."

"If he don't want you to go, Joseph, you better not. I can just go over myself and take a look."

"I don't think he'll mind, Ollie. Especially if I can bring some of our furniture back, or tools or something he needs."

"Well, maybe. Make sure he don't mind though. You ask him."

They parted then and Joseph walked back to his house. It was on his mind that he had made a promise. "All I said was that I wouldn't go off by *myself*," he finally said aloud.

Chapter 4

Joseph, to his own surprise, was able to get his father's permission to go to the landing. Father said Joseph could go if he left early and got back before noon. Joseph suspected that his father regretted not letting Joseph get away once in a while, and that he was granting the holiday as a sort of payment for all his work. He also knew that Father felt a certain obligation to Ollie and was probably sorry that he had not been friendlier to him. But Joseph also knew that there was no way that he could make it to the old settlement in Jackson County and back again by noon. He would just have to deal with that problem when the time came. If he could bring some things back, maybe Father would forgive him rather easily. That was Joseph's hope, at least.

Joseph found Ollie on a filthy old riverboat called the *San Juan*. The sun was just coming up, but Ollie was up and ready, standing on deck when Joseph arrived. He was wearing a red flannel shirt, just like the ones he had always worn in Jackson County.

"You still want to go back to your old place?" Ollie asked.

"I surely do."

"Well, I talked to the ferryman here, and he says he'll cross us over and give us a horse for the day for half a dollar."

"I have no money, Ollie."

"You can leave that to me."

"I'll pay you back some day, Ollie."

"That's no problem."

"But we need a wagon."

31

"Well, I thought about that. A wagon's slow and it'd cost us extra to ferry across the Big Blue. I know where we can ford the Blue with a horse. We can ride double and still be back afore nightfall. And if we find quite a load still over there, we'll stash it somewheres—maybe up in the caves. If it ain't much, we can just tote it along on the horse."

That sounded good to Joseph. After Ollie gave Joseph a quick tour of the boat, the two headed for the ferry. Colonel Allen now had a ferry with a wheezing little steam engine on it. Crossing hardly took any time at all compared to what it had with the old raft ferries. In less than half an hour they were across the river. Ollie paid the old fellow his half dollar, and the man eyed it carefully and then dropped it in his vest pocket.

Ollie saddled the old horse; neither the horse nor the saddle was in very good shape, but they would have to do. Joseph clung to Ollie's waist as Ollie drove his heels into the horse's flanks, but the horse set off at a steady walk and never altered his pace in spite of all the clucking and nudging that Ollie could do. Ollie knew the quickest way, cutting through the woods in places and following the road in others. By ten o'clock the boys were crossing the prairie Joseph remembered so well and approaching the old Colesville settlement. Joseph could see his house near the edge of the woods. "It's still standing. They didn't burn it down," Joseph said.

"But I don't see your wagon, Joseph."

It was true. Joseph was apprehensive as the old horse plodded toward the house. He hated to think that nothing was left. And then Ollie said, "There's part of your wagon—the bed of it; somebody's toted off all the wheels."

Joseph slipped off the horse and ran to the wagon, which was almost grown over with grass and weeds. He looked into the decaying old wagon bed and found that it was empty—or almost. There was a short length of rope and a torn piece of canvas that Father might like to have. Joseph picked up the rope but found that it was rotted and useless. He turned and looked toward the house. The glass windows were gone. The door stood halfway open. Joseph walked into the relative darkness and let his eyes adjust. The furniture was all gone: the beds, the chairs, everything. Joseph felt sick. The room smelled of decay and of damp wood. Joseph knew that the wind had blown snow in all winter on Mother's prize puncheon floor—the floor she had scrubbed and swept until it was almost white.

Ollie walked in behind Joseph. "Everything pretty much gone?"

"It's *all* gone, Ollie. People just came in and stole everything. Just like rats." Joseph wanted to curse them, wanted to have a chance to fight a few of them.

"I guess it's what most folks would do. They figured you wasn't coming back anyhow, and if they didn't take it somebody else would for sure."

"That doesn't make it right."

"No, I guess it don't. See anything you can take back?"

"Just some old canvas out in the wagon."

"That ain't much. Let's look around a little more."

Joseph walked over to the fireplace and looked in. There was a nest of mice in the corner and that was all. Along the base of the walls, on the north and east sides of the cabin, leaves were piled at least a foot high. Joseph kicked at the leaves, but found nothing under them. "Give me a lift up to the loft, Ollie. Our ladder is even gone."

Ollie cupped his hands together and Joseph stepped into them. Ollie hoisted him up high enough that Joseph could pull himself the rest of the way. It was darker up above, but a few cracks in the roof gave him enough light to have a look around.

"See anything?" Ollie called from below.

"No—it's the same up here. It's stripped clean." Ollie helped him down, and they walked out into the sunlight. "It's unfair, Ollie. Why do things always have to be so unfair?"

"I don't know, Joseph. 'Cept I know the folks that took everything always figured you was the unfair ones."

Joseph knew all that. He had been over it a thousand times. The old settlers thought that the Mormons were trying to come in and take over the county, that they would push the old settlers out. And maybe it was true, in a way. Father said that they had intended to buy the lands for a fair price, not drive the people out, but the fact was that the Mormons did want to have the place and the old settlers did not want to give it up. But the one clear reality to Joseph was that he and his family had lost everything and someone had gained by that loss. It simply was not fair.

"One thing I do know, Joseph. It don't do no good to think too much on it. I guess my pa was wrong in what he done to you *and* to me, but I got me a job now, one I don't mind much, and so it's sorta all right. You just got to go on sometimes and not always be fretting about what's done and gone."

"I know all that, Ollie. That's plain as day to me. But it just seems like if there's going to be lots of unfair things in this world that sometimes *I* ought to be the one that comes out ahead."

"I 'spose things kind of even out in the long run, Joseph. Anyhow, the preachers all say you ain't 'sposed to think on it thataway. You're 'sposed to like it better when somebody else comes out on top. Ain't that how you been taught?"

Joseph didn't answer for a moment. He looked at the place where his father had fallen, where Joseph had seen him lying still, with blood running down the side of his head. He remembered Matthew swinging the ax and the horses kicking up dust as they danced backwards in their fear. The place was all overgrown with grass now. It wasn't really the same place at all. It had only been six months, but a great deal had changed.

"I guess maybe some people are better at doing what they ought to do than others, Ollie. Matthew always does the right thing, but me, I can't help it, I still want to come out ahead at least some of the time. Matthew says that whatever God wants is what will happen and we just have

34

to accept it. But me, sometimes I feel like telling God he could run this whole show better than he does. That's why Matthew's going to be a great man and I never will."

Joseph strolled out across the long grass toward the wagon again. He would at least take back the canvas. "Well, Joseph," Ollie said, "I don't know nothing about church and all that. I just go along and try to come out the best I can."

"Then how come you paid half a dollar to bring me over here today?"

Ollie wouldn't answer. "Let's look around out here a little," he said.

Joseph pulled at the canvas, but it ripped all the way across. It was as rotten as the rope. Joseph had nothing to take back.

"What's this here?" Ollie asked. He had found something up against the back of the wagon bed under the grass. He tugged and then stood up holding a wooden box.

"Oh, Ollie, it's Mother's dishes."

Ollie gave the box a little shake and they both heard the rattle. "It sounds like they's all broke up, or mostly so. I guess the box got rolled off the back of the wagon and no one saw it—or else someone gave it a shake like I just did and didn't want it."

"Well, let's take them back anyway. Mother will want to have what's left. Maybe some aren't broken, or maybe some can be fixed."

"We might as well open 'er up and see what we got, 'fore we tote it clear back."

"No, let's not, Ollie. Let's just take it back. Mother would rather have the pieces than nothing. She left everything behind, Ollie—everything she ever had."

Ollie and Joseph walked through the settlement, glancing around, checking each cabin briefly. All the cabins had been stripped the same way. Anything that was still lying about was too useless to bother with. And so the boys mounted the old horse again and plodded back to the river. They saw very few people along the way, and those they saw paid no attention to them. But it was well into the afternoon when they were able to catch the ferry again and cross back into Clay County. The ferryman said that Ollie could keep the horse long enough to give Joseph a ride back to his home.

As the boys approached the Williamses' old shed, Joseph could see Matthew out in back chopping wood—a chore that normally fell to Joseph. He knew that he was in trouble, and he doubted the dishes would be enough to save him.

Matthew came around to the front of the house as Joseph was getting down from the horse. "Joseph, where have you been?" In a moment the whole family had come out.

"We have been worried," Mother said. "Whatever—"

"Joseph, where have you been all day?" Father broke in. "You gave me a promise to be back here by noon."

"It's my dishes," Mother suddenly said. "Joseph, where did you get them?"

"He's crossed the river," Matthew said. "He told me he wanted to do it, but I told him not to."

"Joseph," Father said, "is that true?"

"Yes, sir."

"You lied to me, Joseph. You told me you were going to see Ollie's riverboat."

"I did see it."

"That doesn't change anything, Joseph. You know very well that I would not have let you go had you told me you wanted to cross that river into Jackson County."

"But we had no trouble at all. Ollie knows all the back ways to get there. No one bothered us at all."

"You don't understand, do you, Joseph. I guess you never will." Father took a step forward and pointed into Joseph's face. His dark eyebrows pushed together over his nose as his forehead wrinkled. Joseph could see the anger in Father's tense, dark eyes and in his set jaw under the heavy blackness of his beard. "Rebellion runs right to your very soul. You defy me at every turn. You seem to take joy

36

in acting the enemy to those who love you. I have tried to be patient with you, Joseph, but you push too far."

"Father, I only wanted to see if I could—"

"I know very well what you wanted. Do you think I've never thought of going back to the old place? But I decided the chance was not worth it. And in this house you should look to me for such decisions."

Mother was gone now. She had taken the box into the house and Ruth had gone with her. Father and Matthew stood side by side, solid as a wall, staring at Joseph.

"Father, I thought I could save you some work. I thought maybe I could bring back some of our furniture or tools or something. I just hated to see somebody get off with everything we ever had."

"Joseph, listen to yourself. You still don't understand. Obedience, Joseph. Do you even know the meaning of that word? You'd better learn it soon or you're destined for trouble not only in this life, but in the next."

Joseph knew better than to persist, but he was not convinced. He simply did not believe that he was as bad as Father said he was. Certainly he was no Matthew, but it did not seem to him that Father needed to treat him as an enemy. Joseph decided to say nothing, however, and let some time pass. He felt sad more than anything else, sad that the same old pattern was repeating itself, the same old accusations.

"Now, as for you, Ollie," Father said. "I don't ever want to see you around here again. You may have helped us once, but you knowingly took my boy right back into the middle of hell today. I am afraid you are still your father's son."

Ollie nodded, clucked at his horse, and turned its head to go. Joseph, suddenly very angry, grabbed the bridle near the bit and held the horse where it was. "Wait, Ollie. All right, Father, I lied to you and I went sneaking back across the river. I admit that. I thought it was the right thing to do, and that's why I did it. But Ollie wanted to go alone and I talked him into letting me go with him. He even

thought it was all right with you—he told me to get permission. He spent a half dollar of his own money, and he
did it just because he wanted to help us. Now if you turn
him away and treat him like some thief—some enemy—
you are no better than his pa you hate so much."

"Joseph," Matthew said. "Hush up."

"It's true, Father. You tell me I shouldn't hate. You say
it's not Christian. But you sat in this old shed and hated
everyone and everything all winter. You're full of hate
right now—and it's not fair. Ollie is the best—"

"That's enough, Joseph," Father said loudly, and then
he took a deep breath and for a moment seemed unsure
how to react. Joseph thought that Father might strike out
with his fist, which was doubled and poised near his
shoulder.

"Let me go, Joseph," Ollie said, and he reached down
and pulled Joseph's hand from the bridle. "I'm sure sorry I
caused all this trouble. I won't bother you no more, sir."
He plunged his heels into the horse's sides forcefully
enough that it actually set off at a gallop.

Father stood looking at Joseph, and Joseph suspected
that his father's reprimand was just beginning, but then he
saw tears in his father's eyes. Joseph did not know what it
meant, what Father was thinking.

"Joseph, you fool," Matthew said. Joseph was stunned.
His brother's voice was bitter, full of hatred, it seemed. "I
told you not to do such a foolish thing, and you promised
me. And now you come home and talk to Father like that.
You have no right to . . ."

But Matthew stopped when he saw his father quietly
turn and walk toward the house. Joseph wanted to run
after him and say that he was sorry, but he could not do it.

"Look what you've done, Joseph. How could you say
such things to him?" Joseph didn't answer; he was wondering the same thing himself. "You promised me, Joseph.
You stood right here and said you wouldn't go over to the
old settlement."

For an instant Joseph almost broke down, almost

38

apologized, almost cried. And then for some reason that he did not understand, he shot back, "I only said I wouldn't go back *alone,* Matthew. Leave me alone, will you?"

Matthew stared at him, blocked in front of him with hands on his hips and his forehead butting forward. "You don't even know a lie when you tell one, Joseph. You twist words around and think that makes things right. What kind of mission do you think you can serve if you keep this up?"

"You can have my *mission,* Matthew. I told you that a long time ago." He stepped around Matthew and walked into the house. Mother had pried open the box and found the hundreds of pieces of her china. Tears were running down her cheeks and falling into the box.

Chapter 5

For the next few days Joseph watched his father carefully. Father seemed subdued, quiet. He was working hard each day, but some of the vigor he had begun to show was now waning. Joseph knew that he was tired from trying to go back to work, but there was more to it than that. He often looked thoughtful. He would stop in his work, wipe his forehead with the flat of his hand, and then stare down toward the river and apparently forget what he was doing. He was not just resting; he was thinking. But through it all he said almost nothing to Joseph.

Spring planting was in full swing now, and Father was trying to get his crops in. The potatoes were already in the ground, but corn was the big crop, and it took many days to plow and sow almost twenty acres. He was trying to remove some of the stumps that were still in the field, but there was no way he could get them all out. He had to simply plow around many of them. Colonel Allen had loaned Father a mule and a plow; it had not been easy for Father to accept them, but he had a family to feed, and that left him little choice. But he told Colonel Allen he wanted to buy the mule, that he would pay at harvesttime, if that would be agreeable. The Colonel said that would be fine. And so Father arose early each day and plowed the fields north and south and then east and west. Matthew and Joseph sowed the seed behind him. The three of them also planted a garden, and now Joseph had begun the first tedious days of weeding. A vicious rainstorm passed through one night and washed out part of the garden and more than an acre of the planted corn. Father said very little about it; he just let the sun dry the ground for a day, and then replowed the land and planted again.

But by noon each day Father was exhausted. He would lie down after eating his dinner and fall asleep. Some afternoons he slept for three hours before he could get up and go back to work. And he seemed to work with resolution rather than with enthusiasm. These were the blessed days in Missouri when the weather was mild and the hills were a blend of copper and green as the first buds were opening up in the oak and hickory forests. In Jackson County Father had stood outside the house on such days, after the evening meal, and had spoken of his land with reverence and satisfaction. He had often become almost excited as he had described the future: the farm as it someday would be, and the society that would make up the city of God. But now he seemed only to work to get the job done.

Matthew and Joseph had missed school the previous winter, but Father talked now of getting a school started for the next fall. He wanted his boys to have a proper education, he said. But here again there was a tone of resolution in his voice, a sense of duty more than the sound of enthusiasm. To Joseph he seemed almost frightened, desperate to make the best of things, but not hopeful, or at least not full of faith in the future.

Joseph wanted to talk to his father. He knew that he had never apologized to him, and he knew it was something that he had to do. But Father was so aloof these days that Joseph could not bring himself to attempt to break through to him. Finally, however, Father talked to Joseph. He had been teaching Matthew to plow, how to harness and handle the old mule, and how to guide the shear. When he finally turned Matthew loose in the field one morning, Father called Joseph to his side.

"Joseph, I want you to watch your brother here for a few minutes. I want you to learn this too. I suspect you won't grow up to be a farmer, but you may need to farm a good deal for the next few years. Now watch as he turns the mule at the end of the field."

"Why don't you think I'll be a farmer?"

"Just watch now. You see how he's doing that? He needs to pull old Sally back around a little sooner, but he has the idea." He stared off down the field, and Joseph saw that far-off look come over his face. Joseph turned and started back up the gentle slope to the garden. "Joseph, wait here a minute or two. I want you to watch. As soon as Matthew can make out all right I want you to try your hand at this." Joseph stood and watched as Matthew and the mule worked their way back across the field. Joseph liked to watch the black earth fold back as the plow passed through. But he had little desire to learn to plow; he knew what hard work it was. He could see Matthew struggling to hold the handles straight and to keep a steady furrow.

"Joseph, you are a restless boy, and you are intelligent. I would say right now that you will either do something very good with your life or something very bad. A boy with your spirit will want to get out and do something, accomplish some things. I can't imagine you farming all your life."

Joseph rather liked hearing this. He had known for some time that he wanted no part of farming. And yet he had no idea what else he could do. He would like to work on the river, but he knew what his father would think of that.

"That's better, Matthew," Father called out. "Pull her around, show her when she needs to cut out. You're getting better." Joseph was glad to see Father coming out of his quiet mood. At least he seemed to want to talk, and he seemed to care about Matthew's improvement. All the same, Joseph still felt very little sense of renewed happiness in Father's tone and manner. There was a hint of melancholy in all he said.

"Joseph, if you can learn to bridle yourself and to accept your leaders' guidance, you can do almost anything you like in this life. But if you do not, you will always be

42

running off, trying to do too much on your own, too caught up in yourself to worry about anyone else." He stopped and watched Matthew, but Joseph knew that more was coming. He sensed that this was a speech that Father had been preparing for some time—maybe ever since the day Joseph had accused him of being full of hate.

"In most ways you are more like your mother than like me. But I've found out in the last year that I have a streak of rebelliousness myself, just as I have accused you of having. I never have liked to let anyone else do much of anything for me. I am allowing it now because I have to, but I don't like it. I would just rather take care of my own affairs."

"That's not so bad, is it?"

"Well, no. Not exactly. But there is pride in it, Joseph. We all should look after each other, which means that there are times when you simply have to accept help as well as give it. It's brought me down hard to fall on those times, Joseph. I've never gone through anything like it before."

"You're almost back to full strength now, Father. You'll be out helping other folks and paying back before long."

Father didn't answer. He took off his hat and ran his hand across his forehead. Joseph saw his eyes focus on the distant trees along the Missouri. He was standing too low in the field to see beyond the river, but Joseph knew he was trying to see back to Zion, as Joseph often did. "No, Joseph, I'm not back to full strength. Those men stole the power from my body and it's not coming back, not like it was. I suppose it's what God wanted me to learn—to have to be brought down like this. But Joseph, you need to learn some of the same things. Maybe I have no right to say very much to you, since I haven't accepted the lesson yet myself. But we both need to do what we can to change."

So this was it; this was why Father had not spoken sooner. This was what he wanted to say. "Father," Joseph said, "I think you are a great man."

Father looked down at Joseph and quietly studied the boy's face for a moment. "That's not what you told me when you said I was no better than Oliver Markley."

"I was just angry when I said that."

"But son, that doesn't change the fact that you were right. I *am* full of hate. I've tried to fight it—I am still trying—but I haven't come very far." His eyes went back to Matthew and the field. "No, Matthew," he yelled. "You let her get away that time. She rounded off too wide on you."

"Father, you have a right to be angry about what they did to you. You never would do anything like that yourself."

Father smoothed down his beard, as he had a habit of doing. "That, Joseph, is what I do not know. I gave up my trade and almost everything I had to come to Zion. The only thing I had left was my energy and strength, but that has always been enough for me. I can't seem to stop dwelling on that—that they took the one thing I still possessed that could keep me going, and could keep my family going. When I think about that I get angry enough to hurt someone—or to try."

"But you wouldn't do it, Father. I know you wouldn't. The only reason I got so angry with you was that you said those things about Ollie. You have a right to hate his pa, but not Ollie."

"Now that's where you're wrong, Joseph. And that's what I am trying to tell you. I don't have the right to hate anyone. That's the whole reason we take on the name of Christ—to stop hating, even our enemies."

"But how can you do that? How can anybody do that?"

"I don't know, Joseph, but I do know that you and I need to do some learning. We'd better figure it out, son."

"I guess Ollie hates less than most people I know of," Joseph said.

Father did not respond for some time, but finally he said, "Well, I wish you would choose Bishop Partridge for

44

your example, son. He's the man I admire in this regard. I know that Ollie has his good qualities, but I don't think he is good for you. He's cut loose—and yet still just a boy himself. Riverboating sounds desirable, you know, and maybe looks exciting to a boy on a farm, but it's not solid. It's not the right way to find your place and then make something worthwhile in this life. You can't be just wandering about like that, not if you want to be one of the Saints. We have to all work together, even if maybe people like you and I would almost rather run off on our own. Ollie could bring out the worst in you, I fear, even though you say he is a good fellow, and I suppose he is."

Joseph understood, but he couldn't quite agree. He couldn't argue either; he didn't even have an argument. But he liked Ollie and he felt a fierce loyalty to him, and for Joseph, that was all there was to the matter. It did not seem possible that Ollie could be good and yet, for some reason, someone to avoid.

"Joseph, I want you to stay away from riverboats. Rivermen are polluted as any breed you will find." Then he yelled to Matthew, "That's just right. Now watch that furrow and hold to a straight line."

Joseph joined Father in watching Matthew for a time. Matthew looked like Father from the back as he moved down the field, and Joseph could see his arms fighting the plow, holding the handles as straight as he possibly could. That was the simple way, the right way. "Father, I've been wanting to tell you . . ." Father had taken a step ahead, about to approach Matthew as he came up the row the next time. But now he turned back and looked at Joseph. "I've been wanting to tell you that I'm sorry I lied and went back to our old home. And I'm sorry for all the things I said to you that day."

Father took a step back toward Joseph. "Thank you, son. That's good. That's a good start. But you have been sorry before. I want you to change now and show more sign that you are one of God's chosen people. I had to judge, Joseph, and I judged that the danger was too great for one of

45

us to go back. Can you accept my judgment for now, son?"

"I'll try, Father, but when things seem right to me, I just want to do them and not have anyone tell me I can't."

"Well, that's what we've been talking about, isn't it? Learning to take advice. Learning to obey. But I'll be honest with you, Joseph. Part of why I was so angry was that you had done what I wanted to do. I wished that I could have given Mother her dishes, broken up as they were. I guess the sins of the fathers are visited upon the heads of the sons. You've learned too much from me, son, both of what's good and what's bad. In the time I have left I want to bring you up tall and strong, but at the same time, humble and not proud."

Father then walked across the plowed field, the folded soil that lay in dark black rows. He walked alongside Matthew, talking to him, instructing him. Matthew listened and nodded, accepting the advice.

Joseph thought maybe he had only just come to love his father. Back in the old settlement in Jackson County in the dark one night, he had been overjoyed to discover that his father was still alive, and again on the banks of the Missouri he had felt the same joy. But now he had some sense of who the man was. Joseph wanted to do better; he wanted to be more like Matthew, more like Father.

Father slept some that afternoon and Matthew continued to plow, while Joseph sowed corn. Late in the day, just before supper, Ira Willes came by. He was still recovering from his injuries and was not well enough to work very hard, but Newel Knight sometimes had him carry messages to the Colesville Saints who were not close to the main group.

Brother Willes came to Matthew first, but when he saw that he was not Father he reined up his horse and called out to ask where Brother Williams was. Matthew told him Father was in the house and Brother Willes rode off in that direction. Joseph went to the house himself, wondering what the news was.

46

When Joseph got to the house Brother Willes and Father had just stepped outside. Ira glanced at Joseph and then looked at Father questioningly.

"That's all right. He can hear. What's the trouble?"

"Brother Newel says there ain't likely to be trouble but he don't know but what there could be, and he thought everyone ought to know, so as to be a little on the watch."

"I understand. What has he heard?"

"Well, Joseph Smith and the others have started out now from Ohio, or leastways they's supposed to be, from what we heard. They wanted to get off by around the first of May. He calls his army Zion's Camp, and he—"

"Yes, Ira, I know all that."

"Well, I didn't know what you had or maybe hadn't heard about. Some hears more than others, and I never know for absolute sure who's heard something and who hasn't. When I told Brother—"

"Ira, tell me what the problem is."

"All right, I will. Some of the old settlers back in Jackson—all our old 'friends' like Reverend Pixley, and Pitcher and Lucas and Owens and Boggs—they got wind somehow about the Prophet coming out here. Everyone over there in Jackson started telling about how the Mormons had an army of thousands and was going to come in and kill every woman and child in the county, and stories like that. I guess there's been all kinds of fuss about it. One thing they done was go back—I guess last week sometime—and they burned down all our houses that was still standing. Except the ones people stole and are living in."

"Did they burn our old settlement, or just the ones close to Independence?"

"I guess they burned all of them. Except as I understand it, they left Brother Knight's mill and some gentiles is running it now. There's even some talk that maybe they'll come across the river and attack us before Joseph Smith ever gets out here. They say if the Clay County folks won't drive us out, then they will just have to do it themselves."

47

"Do you know of any actual plans, or is it all just talk?"

"Just talk, so far, I guess. One thing, though—we're more spread out than we was over in Jackson. Newel says that if anyone in our branch sees or hears anything we should put out the word and all gather at his place. I guess the other settlements will do the same."

"Well, thank you, Brother Willes. I never thought they would cross the river to bother us, but with these men, I suppose we should have expected it. They have our land. What more do they want?"

"I don't know, Matthew. Some more of our blood, I guess."

Brother Willes wished everyone well and then left. Father and Joseph were left standing in front of the house. Father looked at Joseph. "You see why I struggle to stop hating, Joseph?"

Joseph felt as though the blood had drained from his head. Somehow this possibility had never occurred to him. He had always assumed that the Saints were safe once they had crossed the river. "Yes, I do, Father," he said.

Chapter 6

The days that followed were not really as frightening as the last months in Jackson County had been, but Joseph felt a gnawing apprehension at the idea that everything could start all over again. At night in the little house he sometimes listened to the steady breathing of all the family members and felt a sense of comfort in the calm, but when the wind blew, or even when Ruth or the baby would stir in their sleep, he would sometimes start, and he would remember the feelings, the very taste in his mouth, of the old fear he had known. He was older now and should not be afraid, he told himself. And he tried to remind himself that there was less to lose now, that this old shed would be easy to give up. All the same, the sense that someone out there, not many miles away, continued to hate him and wish him banished was infuriating during the day and frightening at night.

Almost every day reports reached the Williamses about the movement of Joseph Smith and his Zion's Camp. Some said there were more than four hundred of the brethren coming, but others, including Newel Knight, said the number was far fewer, perhaps two hundred. May and early June passed away before definite word came that the little army had crossed the Mississippi and was in the state.

If there were plenty of rumors about the Mormon army, there were just as many about the preparations for war being made among the Jackson County settlers. Not only were armies being organized, rumor had it that cannons and fortifications were being prepared as well. One story circulated that a large army planned to march across the state and engage Zion's Camp in battle before it could

49

even approach the area. At the same time, some of the Mormons were gathering to make bullets and swords. They had lost most of their weapons to the Jackson mobs; now they felt defenseless, and so they began to forge what weapons they could.

When the Williamses went to church on the fifteenth of June, they were told that a meeting had been called in Liberty for the next day. Clay County leaders would attend, along with representatives from Jackson County, and the Mormon leaders were invited. Peace proposals were to be discussed. The Colesville Branch members did a good deal of speculating that day as to what this would mean. Most of the Saints planned to be at the meeting, but Brother Williams told Joseph and Matthew that he had far too much work to do to be running off to Liberty.

Joseph wondered all the next day what was happening. Late in the afternoon Ira Willes rode up to the house. Father and the two boys were still in the field, but they all three approached Ira, and he simply remained mounted and told his story. "Well, Matthew, the meeting is over, but I am not sure what good came of it."

"What was decided?"

"Nothing. Not really."

"Well, tell us what happened, Ira."

"All right, I will. First off, there was mostly speech making. Old Pixley got up and said how we was a worthless lot of people, murderers and I don't know what all. He said no one would ever be safe until we was all run clear out of here. Some of the other Jackson men said about the same, and so did even a couple of the Clay County folks. But Mr. Doniphan got up and he give a good talk. He said we was fine people and he knew us well and never knew us to be anything but good citizens, good as any around. He said he admired Joseph Smith for wanting to come out here and help his friends."

"What did the crowd think of that?" Father asked.

"Well, some clapped their hands and said that was right, and some was hooting and screaming for him to sit

50

down. It was a wild show. Old Mr. Turnham done a good job too, though. He was in charge. He said that he never wanted to see the folks of Clay County disgrace themselves the way the folks in Jackson had. Old Lucas and Owens and Boggs turned red and started squirming around—they was mad enough to go after him. Things was getting pretty hot and then some fellow comes in the back and says, 'There's a man stabbed out here.' Everybody went running out to see what it was, but there wasn't no Mormons in on it. It was two old settlers, I think from here in Clay, and the one had cut the other pretty good with a dirk."

"So that was the end of it?"

"That's all that happened. Except the boys from Jackson did have a proposal. What they said they wanted to do was buy up all our lands for twice the price. They went on about how it would all be fair and they would have a committee to judge the price with some of the Saints helping out and all. Then they said if we didn't want that, we could buy them out on the same terms."

"Where would we ever get the money to do that?"

"We wouldn't. And of course they know that. And we can't sell either, and we can't promise never to come back the way they wanted us to. It's still Zion, and the Prophet says we will go back sometime. So there we are. Nothing's changed."

"I guess nothing has," Father said. "I suppose the next step is war."

"Might be," Ira said. He glanced at each of the boys, who were standing on opposite sides of Father. "I guess we can win, though. I guess God will help us."

"I wish it were that simple," Father said.

Ira looked at Father curiously, cocking his head a bit to one side. But he only said, "Well, I got to get on home. Newel says to tell you that trouble just might come up any time now. Head for his place if you hear of anything. You're in kind of a bad spot out here by yourselves." Father agreed and Brother Willes rode away.

In the next few days the news was even more frightening. The Jackson delegation's boat had sunk in recrossing the Missouri River. How many of them had drowned was not known, but some had. It was difficult for the Mormons not to take delight in what seemed to them God's vengeance. The story had gone about that James Campbell, one of the delegation, had vowed to leave his flesh to be eaten by the eagles and buzzards if he did not "fix Joe Smith and his army so that their skins would not hold shucks." But Campbell had drowned and, according to the story, he had been found in a clump of driftwood where the animals and birds had eaten most of his body away. The problem with all this was that the Jackson County people believed that the Mormons had bored holes in the boat and thereby murdered the men who had drowned. This only heightened the animosity on both sides of the river.

On Thursday of that week, Zion's Camp had entered Clay County, far north and east of where the Williamses lived. On the same day John Whitmer stopped by on his way to visit Newel Knight. He said the warning was going out. Armed men had been seen crossing the river from Jackson County into Clay County that day. The trouble was likely to be in the north of the county, near Fishing River where the Prophet's army was camped, but everyone was to be ready.

No more was heard that day. Father continued his work. The corn was in now, and the first shoots were coming up. Joseph had been given the tedious task of watching the lower field near the woods. Gray squirrels loved to come out of the woods and feed on the young cornstalks. Joseph had made a sling to throw stones at the pests, but he soon learned the squirrels were too smart for that. They would dodge the stones and go right on eating. He would have to run at them directly to scare them away, and by then another two or three would be back in the field in other places. The job soon became exasperating and tiresome. And all day Joseph wondered whether he would ever see the corn reach maturity anyway; maybe they would be driven out of Clay County just as they had been driven out of Jackson.

After supper Joseph noticed that thunderheads were building and advancing from the northwest. Huge billows, charcoal-colored underneath, spread all across the western sky, the sunset tinting them orange. The sky, in patches, had taken on a curious green tone, evil and ominous looking. Lightning lashed along the underside of these thunderheads almost incessantly. Father and the boys gathered in the tools and brought the mule into her lean-to by the house. The first rain was already falling, only lightly, but by the time Joseph headed for the house, big drops had begun to plop on the dust by the front door.

The first few waves of the storm were not terribly intense, but as the evening continued the wind picked up and the rain came down so violently that the little shed quivered with the vibration. The roof leaked in more places than there were pans to catch the drips, and in some places the water was even forced in through the cracks in the walls. At times the wind seemed destined to blow the whole shed away. Joseph could actually see the walls shift and hear them groan under the pressure. But worst of all was the wild lightning; the flashes penetrated the cracks of the walls and roof so steadily that it seemed daylight outside, and all the while the thunder was roaring and crashing.

No one slept, of course. Little Samuel was terrified by the noise. He cried steadily and clung to his mother. Ruth tried to crowd her way onto Mother's lap until Father took her. She buried her head against her father's chest and cupped her hands over her ears. Everyone sought out a place where no drips were falling, but finally it was a matter of finding a place where the dripping was lighter than in other places.

Joseph knew that these storms always blew over in time, that it was just a matter of waiting, but this was the worst one ever, and he wondered whether the house could withstand it. Just when the storm seemed to be letting up

53

some, the wind suddenly struck with double force and hail rattled off the clapboards of the roof with a frenzy that seemed too malignant not to be intended by some evil force.

Before morning the storm abated, and in spite of the wet bedding everyone was able to get a little rest. Father had expressed his concern for the crops when the storm had first begun, but as the night had continued and the rain had not let up, he had grown even quieter than usual. Joseph noticed that he looked tired and pale. He had let a drop fall upon his shoulder until it had become a steady dribble, and yet he had not moved until Mother had said something to him about it.

When morning came and Mother and the boys arose, Father did not. This was not usual for him; he would take his rest in the afternoons, but he was normally the first out of bed in the morning. Joseph had expected him to be up early to inspect the crops.

Mother began the usual cornbread breakfast, deciding to let Father get some needed rest. But when he rolled over once and moaned, she went to him and touched his shoulder. "Matthew, are you all right?" He didn't answer. She touched his forehead with the palm of her hand. "Oh, Joseph," she said. "Your father is sick again; he's burning up."

Joseph walked to her side and felt his father's forehead. Father stirred a little and opened his eyes. "Matthew," Mother said, "how do you feel?"

He stared at her for a moment, not comprehending, his eyes not really focusing on her. He moaned again, and then turned on his side. "Oh, Matthew, not again. Please, not again," she said, and for a few seconds she covered her face with her hands. Then she turned to Joseph. "Get some fresh water from the rain barrel."

All that day Father lay sick. He spoke with Mother when she urged him to, but he had little to say. He seemed only partially aware of what he was hearing. She fed him a bit of mush, but he vomited violently afterwards. And so

54

she sat by him most of the day and bathed his head with cool water.

Matthew had gone out early that morning to look at the fields. He came back and told Mother that the corn was beaten down, but it was young enough that it would come back all right. The worst problem was that a stream had formed, angling across the bottom part of the field, and it had washed out part of the crop. It had cut not a wide swath, but a deep one. Matthew had no idea what they would do to build it back up. He wished that he could talk to Father, but he did not try.

There was little the boys could do; the fields were too muddy to work in. Finally Mother asked them to take the little ones out of the house. She said she had heard that cholera had been breaking out in the county again. It might be what Father had, and she did not want the children near him.

It was a long day, with too much idle time. Joseph was worried. In the afternoon Ira Willes came by to report the latest news. Joseph went to the house after Brother Willes left; he wanted to tell Mother.

"Mother, Brother Willes was just here." Joseph stood in the doorway but didn't go inside. She looked at him, obviously preoccupied, but she asked, "What did he say?" Her hair had come out of its usual tight roll, and she looked tired, or maybe frightened.

"He said the storm stopped the Jackson army. They got hit so hard with hail and wind they waited out the storm and then turned tail and went back across the river. The Fishing River rose so high they couldn't even cross it to get near Joseph Smith and his army." It had been a fine story when Ira Willes had told it, but now Joseph tried to laugh and couldn't.

"Joseph, you'd better not come too near. The way he has been vomiting, I'm afraid it *is* the cholera."

"How is he doing, Mother?"

"He's not well at all, Joseph. He seems sicker than he ever was before. It's either that or he's not fighting back at all." Mother's eyes focused intensely on Joseph, as though she had something more to say. Her voice had revealed her fear, but it seemed touched with something else. She sounded almost angry.

"He'll be fine, Mother," Joseph said, when his mother finally showed no sign of continuing, but he was haunted by her look and tone for the next two days as Father continued the same.

At times Father became coherent and seemed to be coming out of the depths of his illness, but then he would sink back into a sleep that was like a coma. Mother had to keep Samuel with her to feed him, but the boys slept outside in the lean-to, and Ruth slept there with them.

On Sunday Hezekiah Peck and Newel Knight came and anointed Father's head with oil and then laid their hands upon his head and blessed him. But as night approached there was no change in him. The fever lessened at times, but little life seemed to return. Joseph knew, everyone knew, that Father was at the very door of death, but no one said it. Joseph kept thinking of the talk that he and Father had had on the day they had watched Matthew plow. Joseph had always been frightened by the thought of losing Father, but now he ached with something beyond fear. He wanted more such talks, more of that kind of closeness.

Father continued unchanged all day Monday. He awoke and talked for a while, but he was soon exhausted and fell back to sleep. Mother tried to feed him a little soup, but he only vomited it up. On Tuesday and Wednesday he remained about the same. As dawn broke Thursday morning Joseph was awake, and he sensed that Matthew was too.

"Matthew?"

"What?"

"Do you think Father will die?"

"I don't know. He's awfully sick."

Joseph had not wanted Matthew to say that; he wanted Matthew to reassure him. Joseph lay there thinking about Father. He remembered again what he had said: "I want to bring you up strong and tall, but humble and not proud." Father had to live; his death was unthinkable. Joseph felt almost panicked with desire to do something.

"Matthew, they say Joseph Smith is camped not too far from Liberty. If I got on old Sally, in two or three hours I could find him. If I asked him to, he would come here; I'm sure of it. He could bless Father and raise him up."

"Joseph, the brethren already blessed him."

"I know, but just Brother Knight and Brother Peck. If Joseph Smith did it, he's the Prophet, and he could—"

"It's the same priesthood, Joseph."

"I know it is, but Brother Joseph can do things other men can't. You know that."

"He can't change the Lord's will, Joseph. The brethren blessed Father and there was no change. Maybe there will be yet, but it makes me fear that Father's time has come. Maybe he should have died last fall; maybe God only let us keep him long enough to get through the hardest times."

"Matthew, I can't stand to hear you say that. You're just giving up. Why don't we at least try to do something. Brother Joseph could—"

"We have to accept God's will, Joseph. We can't change it. It's what Father keeps trying to teach you."

"Well, we can try. I mean, we can do *something*, not just wait and take whatever comes." And then Joseph realized that Mother was near them, just outside the lean-to. Joseph scrambled out. "How is he, Mother?"

She was pale. Her eyes were deeply ringed and her hair was all fallen down in back. She only stared at Joseph.

"He's not gone, is he?"

"No," she said, "but he's sinking. He'll be gone soon." She sounded worn out, resigned, and yet there was still a harshness in her voice that sounded like anger.

"No he won't, Mother. Don't say that. Come on now, don't say that. We'll do something. I'm going to get on Sally and I'm going to find Joseph Smith. He'll come. He'll bless Father."

"It was Joseph Smith who sent us out here in the first place," she said with sudden vehemence. It was the old doubt, the old regret, but Joseph had not suspected that it still lingered in Mother.

"But he can save Father. I know he can. I'm going." Joseph had slept in his clothes; now he began searching about for his boots.

"You are not going *anywhere*, Joseph," Matthew said. He crawled out from the lean-to. "Brother Joseph cannot leave his army to come here. You know that."

"It wouldn't take long. He'll come if he knows how sick Father is. I know he will. I'm going, Matthew. I have to try to do something. Don't make me sit here and wait for Father to die." Joseph was crying, but he didn't know that he was. He was tugging at his boot, but his hands were shaking so badly that he couldn't get it on. Finally he stood up and stamped his foot down to force his heel into the boot. "I'm going," he said again. For one moment he looked directly at Matthew, then at his mother. Tears were running down his cheeks now. Then he began to run toward Sally, who was across the corral.

"Joseph, stop," his mother screamed. She sounded almost wild. Joseph did stop, and he spun around to look at her again. She was not crying, the emotion finding no vent, but her eyes had come to life with passion. "Don't you think you've done enough?" she shouted. "You stay here as you are told." Ruth had gotten up, alarmed by Mother's shouting. She clung to Mother's leg, but Mother seemed not to notice her. "You're the one who has done this, Joseph. You might as well face that."

Joseph didn't comprehend what she was saying. He didn't want to understand. She meant something terrible; he stood stunned by his own suspicion of what she was saying to him.

"You told him he was no better than the Jackson mob. You told him he was full of hate. And he believed you, Joseph. He believed you." Her voice was calm now. She knew what she was saying. She was using her words carefully,

58

like a knife. "He's never been the same since. He gave up because of you, Joseph. He quit trying; he quit caring. He's not fighting back. You killed him, Joseph. You did it, so you be proud of yourself."

Joseph was paralyzed. He was mumbling, "No, Mother, no," but he was twisting with pain inside. His mind was racing. It couldn't be true. She couldn't mean it. Father would be all right. He had to get better. His whole body quivered and he cried audibly, "No, Mother. Please, no. Don't say that. I know he'll live. I'll get help. I'm going now. Keep him alive until I get back. I'll hurry." But Joseph didn't run; he walked to the mule, and his eyes were so blurred he could hardly see.

He heard his mother begin to say something more, but Matthew said, "No, Mother, no." And then he said, "Let him go, Mother. He is never satisfied until he finds things out for himself."

Chapter 7

Joseph rode Sally bareback, with only a rope halter for a bridle. He had to kick her constantly to make her keep up a fair pace. But in about an hour he was in Liberty, and he soon found that almost everyone there knew exactly where Joseph Smith's camp was. The man at the general supply store told him, "Sure, I know where they're at. But I hope you're not planning on going out thataway. From what I been hearing today, they've got the cholera." By pressing the man, Joseph got him to reveal that they were camped at the Burket farm, near Sidney Gilbert's place, about two miles outside Liberty. The storekeeper told Joseph what road he could take to get there, but then he warned him again not to go.

Joseph, of course, set out immediately. It was not yet eight o'clock in the morning when he found the main camp along Rush Creek at the Burket farm. He soon found out that Joseph Smith was at Sidney Gilbert's house nearby, but again he was warned to stay away. And again he ignored the warnings and went directly to Brother Gilbert's place.

Several men—men Joseph didn't know—were standing in front of the house. As Joseph rode into the yard a young fellow who was standing near the gate called out, "Boy, you better stay back. We got sickness here. You better turn that mule around right now."

Joseph kicked his mule and continued straight toward the house. The young man ran up and grabbed the halter rope and stopped the mule; he patted Sally's head as he said, "Son, you better stay back. Did you hear me?"

"I need to see Brother Joseph," Joseph said.

"Are you one of the Saints, son? What's your name?"

"Yes. I'm Joseph Williams. I'm from the Colesville Branch. Where's the Prophet? I need to see him."

"He's busy now, Joseph, meeting with some of your Clay County brothers. You best hurry away. We got cholera here."

"So do we—maybe. My father's dying."

"Well, it won't do no good to come here. Go back to your settlement and get help there. The Prophet has more'n he can handle right now."

"You have to let me see him." Joseph slid down from the mule and ran toward the house, but another man caught him.

"Whoa there, boy. You can't go in there."

Just then Joseph saw Bishop Partridge coming out the door. "Bishop, bishop," Joseph called out.

Bishop Partridge came toward Joseph and put his hand on the boy's shoulder, in his quieting way. "What is it, Joseph?"

"Father's dying. I need to see Brother Joseph."

"It's not a good time to bother the Prophet, Joseph. I'm leaving now. I can go with you to your place. Just let me get my horse and we'll go together. You need to get away from here."

Suddenly Joseph lunged away from the bishop and ran onto the porch and through the open door. Two men were lying on the floor on blankets. Sister Gilbert was kneeling by one of them. She looked up as the boy cried, "Where's Brother Joseph?"

The woman only looked at Joseph, surprised by his sudden presence in her house, and so Joseph ran on past her into the kitchen. As he burst through the door he saw Joseph Smith sitting at the table. William W. Phelps and David Whitmer were across the table from him. "Brother Joseph, I need your help," Joseph said.

Joseph Smith looked pale, not his usual vigorous self,

and young Joseph noticed it immediately. "Joseph Williams," the Prophet said, "you shouldn't be in here. We have cholera here."

"I know that," Joseph said, as Bishop Partridge came in behind him.

"I'm sorry, President Smith," the bishop said, "I tried to—"

"It's all right. What's the problem, Joseph?"

"It's Father. He's going down fast. Mother doesn't know whether it's cholera or not, but he's been sick off and on all this last year, and this time he's dying."

"Has he been administered to by the priesthood?" The Prophet stood up and walked over to Joseph.

"Yes, Brother Knight and Brother Peck blessed him. But it didn't do anything. If you would come you could raise him up. I *know* you could. You've got to come right away or it'll be too late."

"Joseph, if the brethren already blessed him and—"

"But if you do it, it'll be different. You're the Prophet. You can . . ." Joseph lost his words. He was shaking and starting to cry again. "You're the Prophet," he finally repeated.

"Now listen, Joseph." The Prophet bent down to look Joseph directly in the eyes. "We have serious problems here. We could still be attacked. Our own people are very sick. We haven't lost any yet, but it appears we are going to. I just can't leave right now."

"I told him I would go with him," Bishop Partridge said.

"Now, that's fine. No one has greater faith than your bishop, and you know that, Joseph. If it's God's will—"

"No, Brother Joseph, please. If he dies, I killed him. Mother said so. You can't let him die. I . . ." His voice broke and he wept openly. Joseph Smith stood straight up again and pulled the boy's head against his vest. "Please, Brother Joseph. Please come. You're the only one who can save him now."

The Prophet held Joseph and patted him gently on the

62

back. "Oh, Joseph, thank you for believing so. I wish the brethren with me in the camp believed as much. Some awful scourge is upon us, Joseph, and I seem powerless to halt it." The Prophet's own voice shook. "Come with me now. Let's walk outside. I want to have a talk with you."

Joseph Smith put his big hand on the boy's shoulder, and the two walked back through the front parlor and on outside. They continued on past the men in front of the house and onto the road beyond the front gate. There was a huge sycamore tree across the road; Joseph Smith took young Joseph there and the two sat down in the short grass under the tree.

"Joseph, what makes you think you have killed your father?"

"Brother Joseph, if you came with me we could make it fast. You would be back in maybe three hours and—"

"Now Joseph, I told you that I am going to send Bishop Partridge with you, but I want you to tell me about this first."

"I told Father that he was hateful. I said he was no better than the men who beat him last year."

"Was it true?"

"Not really. Not as bad as I made it sound. I was angry when I said it. But it hurt him bad—he said I was right and he knew it. Now Mother says he isn't trying to fight back against the sickness because what I said made him so unhappy." Joseph Smith picked up a piece of bark that had fallen from the old sycamore. He shredded it in half and dropped one of the halves between his boots. He seemed to be thinking, but Joseph was nervous with his slowness. "It's my fault if he dies, Brother Joseph. That's why if you could—"

"It sounds as though you and your mother both said some things in anger that you now regret. But Joseph, you have not killed your father."

"Will he be all right, then?"

"I didn't say that. The Lord has granted me no insight into what is about to happen to us. But if your father dies, you must go on and not ruin your life with hating yourself."

"But Brother Joseph, he doesn't have to die." Joseph stood up. "Please come with me."

Joseph Smith still sat on the ground. He looked up at Joseph. "Listen to me for a moment, Joseph. Last night the brothers in the camp began to fall—all at once, as though they had been struck by Satan himself. I went down to the camp by the creek and commanded the men to arise and be healed. But they didn't rise, and they were not healed. In fact, I was struck with the illness myself and I could not continue; I am not well now, Joseph. I had to recognize the truth. God is chastening us. There has been a bad spirit among us, a spirit of contention and doubt. I don't know how long this will last or how many will die before it's finished, but I know we will be sorely humbled before it's over. Maybe *I* will die. Perhaps the Lord is disappointed with my work. I never felt so powerless in my life. The Lord sent a tempest to save us from the armies last week, but now he is rebuking us."

All the while Joseph Smith had been tearing the bark into narrower strips. He seemed far off, as though he were talking to himself more than to Joseph. "But I cannot leave this place, Joseph. And right now I suspect your bishop has more power to rebuke the sickness than I do."

Joseph stood looking down at the Prophet. Suddenly he felt more frustration than hurt, more anger than sorrow. Joseph Smith had no right to talk this way. "I don't believe in you any more," he spat out. "I thought you were a prophet, but you're not."

Joseph Smith leaned his head back against the tree. His powerful blue eyes focused in on Joseph's own eyes. "Joseph, you are not the first to say that to me today. This may be the worst day of my life. We have marched a thousand miles and now the Governor says he won't help us. We can't fight all these old settlers with two hundred men. Half the camp is saying I led them out here for nothing, that my revelations are false. And yet all I know is that we

64

were supposed to come. There's some reason for all this."

Joseph's emotions were confused. He did feel sorry for Joseph Smith, but for now he was too preoccupied with his own worries to care very much about anyone else's. "If you can't save my father, what's the use of you?" Joseph said, almost shouted. "Why should I believe in you?"

"I can't change God's will, Joseph. No one can do that."

"Well, I'm tired of God just letting the old settlers beat us and kill us and drive us out. It's not fair. He shouldn't just let Father die. My mother needs him. I need him."

"We do not know God's reasons sometimes, Joseph. We have to—"

"Trust him? That's what everyone says. But I don't trust him any more. He lets us down every time."

"I know that you trusted him when you saved your brother's life. I've been told about that. You called on Father in heaven that day, didn't you?"

Joseph stood still. He looked at the tree, the loose layers of bark, avoiding the Prophet's eyes. He didn't answer.

"Didn't the Lord help you that day?"

"I don't know."

"But you *do* know. You knew then. Don't you know now?" Joseph Smith stood up. "Now listen to me, Joseph." He looked big now, and some of his color seemed to come back into his face. "You can run from me, but you can't run from the Lord. You know his power; you have felt it before. You still have a great mission to perform if you will only—"

"Mission," Joseph hissed back at Joseph Smith. "I'm tired of hearing about my *mission*. I pulled my brother as far as I could and then Doc Noland took us the rest of the way. That's all I know for sure. And I don't see what difference it makes whether I run from God or not. He won't help us when we need him."

Joseph turned and walked away. He was going to find his mule and get far away from Joseph Smith. Then he heard the Prophet say, "Don't do this to me, Joseph." The words had come from deep within, and they shook with intensity.

Joseph kept walking a few steps and then he stopped. He stood with his back to the Prophet. "I just want my father," he said, not loud enough for Joseph Smith to hear. The tears came then, and he ran back to Joseph Smith and plunged his head against the Prophet's chest. "I just want my father," he said again. "I didn't mean to kill him."

"Joseph, you haven't killed him. Don't take that guilt upon yourself." He held the boy for some time, his big hand softly patting Joseph's head. "The Lord will bless us yet, Joseph. I promise you as a prophet. The worst may not be over, but we will see better days. I promise you." He was holding the boy close still.

After a few minutes the Prophet took Joseph back to Bishop Partridge. He told the bishop to go with Joseph and to plead with the Lord for Brother Williams's life. And he promised to offer up his own prayers. "The boy has been through a great deal, bishop. He's only twelve, and he's trying to carry too big a burden for his size." He lifted Joseph onto his mule, patted the boy's knee, and said, "I'm sorry, Joseph. I'm sorry you have to live through this. But you will be stronger for it; you are going to be a very strong man someday, Joseph." The tears welled up in the Prophet's eyes.

"I'm sorry too," Joseph said. "I mean, for what I said to you." And he *was* sorry. But he was still terribly confused about everything. Beyond it all was an abiding emotion that transcended everything else: he wanted his father to live.

Edward Partridge rode back with Joseph, and he knew a faster way, avoiding Liberty. It was not yet ten o'clock when they got back. Father lay as he had, still, his breathing barely discernible.

"How is he doing?" the bishop asked.

Mother looked blankly back at him. She was sitting by the bed, holding a cloth in her hand. "He's almost gone," she said.

66

Joseph stood in the doorway as Bishop Partridge placed his hands on Father's head, and he listened closely to the quiet words. The bishop seemed to struggle. He never commanded Father to live, never even told him that he would. "If it be thy will," he kept saying to God, until Joseph wanted to interrupt and tell the bishop to command Father to arise.

When the blessing ended, Father slept on and Joseph finally gave way to a growing hopelessness that had already consumed Mother. But he didn't feel sadness so much as a sense of disgust, of futility.

"Sister Williams, you need sleep," the bishop said. "Why didn't you let any of us know you needed help? I am afraid we have all been fussing about other matters lately; we should have come to see how you were doing. I had heard he was sick, but I—"

"I need no help," Mother said.

"Well, let us know if you do, Sister. You need some sleep."

Mother did not argue, but she looked at Bishop Partridge with hollow eyes, as if to say, "What difference does it make?"

Bishop Partridge left. Father awoke later in the day; he spoke rather clearly for a few minutes, talked to his wife about the crops, told her what needed to be done. But before long his speech became slurred and incoherent, and then he fell back to sleep and soon seemed as distant as before.

Chapter 8

Father continued about the same all that evening. Matthew took a hoe and went to the garden, since the sun was not yet down. Joseph soon followed, but he worked at a dawdling pace, not caring about the garden, wondering what was happening in the house. It was an overpoweringly hot and humid evening. Joseph used the heat as an excuse to walk to the rain barrel at times, and each time he looked into the house, but it was always the same. Father remained still and Mother sat by his bed. Ruth stayed on the shady side of the house, sitting with her doll, just holding it in her arms, hardly moving. The heat was bothering her, Joseph knew, but so was the state of things inside the house. Samuel crawled about on the bed where he liked to play, but he too was strangely quiet and withdrawn, as though he sensed what was happening on the bed across the room.

Matthew and Joseph came in at sunset, and not long afterward they tried to go to sleep in the lean-to. Joseph had been bitten all over by chiggers; he lay on top of his blanket, scratching at the bites. But he hardly knew what he was doing. He was just waiting now. He tried to pray once, but it was a hollow and faithless attempt, as empty as himself. He wondered about Matthew, who had worked as diligently as ever, hoeing with exactly the same intensity and sense of purpose as he would have done on any other day.

"Joseph." For a moment he didn't realize who was speaking to him, and then he knew it was Ruth, who was next to him.

"What?"

"Is Papa sick?"

"Yes."

"Is he *very* sick?"

"Yes."

"I know." That was all she said. Joseph wondered how much she did know, how much she understood.

Then Joseph heard his father's voice in the cabin. He started, and then he listened carefully but could catch none of what was said. He scrambled out of bed and ran around the house. "Where are the children?" he heard Father say, just as Joseph stepped through the door.

"Outside. In the lean-to."

"Let me see them. I want to see them."

Joseph hurried to his father's side, then stopped short. Father was staring straight above, seeming not to see anything. His voice had sounded fairly strong, but his face was drawn and white, the skin stretched over the cheekbones, seemingly thin as paper. Joseph had once seen old Sister Polly Knight after she died. She had looked the same way.

Matthew came in with Ruth, and Mother asked them to come over to Father. The three children stood near Father's side and Mother stood at the foot of the bed.

"How are you, Father?" Matthew asked.

"I'm not well, son," Father said, his voice thick.

"You're going to be fine," Joseph said.

Father seemed to ignore Joseph. "Now Matthew," he said, "listen to me. I wanted to teach you more. But don't worry, you can manage." He waited a moment and took a deep breath. "The brethren will help you, but you can do most things. You need to get a place built for your mother. Get started soon, and maybe you can be finished before you get busy with the harvest."

Joseph watched his brother nod seriously, resolutely. He glanced at his mother, who was standing with her arms folded tightly at her waist. She was still staring with tired, desperate eyes. The blue seemed drained from her eyes, and her face looked drab, almost gray.

"I'll do my best. But try to live," Matthew said, not

desperately but reasonably. "I don't feel ready yet, Father."

Father seemed to try to look for Matthew, but his eyes only rolled vaguely in that direction. "I'm sure of you, Matthew. You have great gifts. You are strong and even. You'll be fine."

"But try to live."

"Don't worry, Matthew. I'll try. Where's Joseph?"

"I'm here, Father."

"We talked, son. Things are all right between us, aren't they?"

"I don't know. I shouldn't have said what I did."

"We talked, Joseph. We put that to rest. Now, you be strong. You are the one in the family with a calling. You must be strong. You must learn to accept things."

"I love you, Father," Joseph said. He was hurt enough to cry, but inside he was still raging. "Please don't die. Please fight back. Mother said you weren't fighting back."

"I'm trying, son. But my strength is all gone." He began to breathe more easily, and his eyes went shut.

"Don't die, Father. Don't die," Joseph said, beginning to panic.

"Hush, Joseph," Father said, his voice weaker. "You be strong, do you hear me?"

"Yes."

"Where's little Ruth?"

"She's here, Father," Matthew said.

Father opened his eyes. He lifted his hand and seemed to try to find her. Ruth took hold of his hand. "You be strong too," he said. "You be like your mama, Ruth. All right?"

Ruth nodded. She held her father's hand and stared into his face. She seemed confused, overwhelmed by what she saw.

Father seemed to sink away again, and Joseph wondered whether he was slipping away for good. But after a short time, he spoke.

"Elizabeth, tell Samuel how much I loved him. All of you will have to help him."

Mother did not say anything. She just stood at the foot of the bed and looked at her husband.

"I want to live," Father said. "Elizabeth, I *do*. But if I don't live, I want you to promise me something." He took a breath, and another deeper one. "Elizabeth, if I die I want you to stay with the Saints."

She didn't answer, but her own breath seemed to become labored, as though she were about to cry.

"Elizabeth, are you there?"

"Yes."

"Will you promise me that?" She still didn't answer. "Don't go back to New York. I want the children to be raised in Zion. It was what I brought them here for. Will you promise me that?"

"Matthew, don't die." She said it almost angrily.

"I can't help it, Elizabeth. My strength is all gone. Please promise me. We'll have a beautiful city yet. Promise me you'll raise my children there."

"Don't make me promise, Matthew."

"Don't take it away from me, Elizabeth." His voice grew stronger suddenly. "You must promise me this."

Joseph watched his mother. She gripped her arms tightly around her waist and shuddered, but she finally said, "All right. I promise." There was no affirmation in her voice, only resignation and bitterness.

"You will be fine, Elizabeth. I promise you. Just stay with the Saints and you'll be fine."

"You can't promise me that," Mother said quietly. "No one can promise me that." Father was breathing deeply now. "Matthew, don't die," Mother suddenly said with force. "Eat something now, while you can." She walked around the bed and the children moved back. "Matthew," she said loudly, shaking his shoulder. "Don't sleep yet. I want you to eat something so you can get back your strength." He did not respond. "Matthew, Matthew." Suddenly she was screaming. "You said you would try to live. Don't leave me like this. Don't die." She gripped both his shoulders and shook him. "Don't die, Matthew. You can't do this to me. I won't know what to do. Please, Matthew, wake up. You need to eat." She dropped on her knees by his bed, no longer screaming, but trembling and crying. "Matthew, I won't know what to do. How will I know? You always knew for me. How will I know?"

She was sobbing unrestrainedly now, and young Matthew had taken hold of her shoulders. "No, Mother. Don't do this," he said. "Think of Ruth."

"But I won't know what to do," she said. "How will I know?" She turned around, sitting on the dirt floor, and stared into young Matthew's face. "How will I know, Matthew? He always knew what we should do."

"Don't, Mother. Trust in me if you can."

"He won't die, Mother," Joseph said. "He's going to live." But Joseph didn't believe his own words anymore.

Matthew got Mother to lie down on the bed across the room from Father. He sat by her and let her cry. He told Joseph to take Ruth outside.

The night eventually passed away, but Joseph never slept, at least not the sleep of rest. A daze of dreams and half-awake thoughts spun through his mind. The next morning the wait continued. Father awoke again about ten o'clock and mumbled incoherently. Joseph kept Ruth outside, as Matthew had asked him to do.

Then, about three o'clock in the afternoon, Joseph heard his mother suddenly scream, "No, Matthew, no!" Joseph ran to the house and through the open door. Mother was shaking Father. "No! Matthew, please don't do this to me." She spun around and looked at Joseph, her face full of wonder and fury. "Why?" she said.

Matthew came through the door, crossed the room, and took Mother in his arms. Joseph felt a terrible thumping anger fill his head. He spun away from them. Mother's question, "Why?" was throbbing through his mind. He stepped out the door and spotted the hoe that Matthew

72

had dropped just outside. He grabbed it and raised it high above his head, then he plunged it into the hard-packed clay in the pathway by the door. He jerked the hoe loose, pulled it back, and slammed it into the ground again. The dust whirled up around him. He tore the hoe loose again and once more slammed it into the earth. "It's not fair!" he shouted. "It's not fair!" Again and again he plunged the hoe into the hard ground, ripping up the pathway. "It's not fair!"

Somewhere in the distance, Joseph heard a voice yelling, "Stop it, Joseph! Stop it!" But his mind did not accept it, never really recognized what the words meant. He banged the hoe into the ground again, ripped it loose again, and slammed it back again—and again and again. "It's not fair! It's not fair! It's not fair!" And each time that he plunged the hoe into the ground he timed it with the word "fair." He didn't know he was crying. He didn't know where Matthew was, or Mother, or Ruth, or Samuel. He was alone. He was attacking the hard clay under his feet, slamming the hoe until his arms began to slow without his realizing it. He was exhausted, but again and again he raised the hoe and slammed it down, even after his strength was all but gone.

And then he felt a hand on his shoulder, a firm grasp. He spun back and drove the hoe at his enemy. The handle struck Matthew across the ribs and sent him plunging into the dirt, gasping for air. Joseph stood in a haze of sunlight and swirling dust. He stared at his brother, who was looking up, his face contorted with pain. Joseph wondered what had happened. He felt drained and tired and out of breath. His brother was hurt, lying on the ground.

Joseph dropped to his knees and grabbed Matthew's head and pulled it against his chest. "Oh Matthew, I didn't mean to hurt you."

"I know, Joseph. It's all right."

"But it isn't fair, Matthew. It isn't *fair*. Why couldn't God let him live?"

Chapter 9

Joseph eventually stopped raging, and so did his mother. It was not that he accepted the death or even changed his feelings toward it. He simply discontinued the show of outward rage. But his sense of indignation remained. If this could happen, what might happen next? He had always trusted in God for protection, but now the shield seemed to be lifted, and absolutely any vengeance, any violence, any pain, could apparently be unleashed upon him. What had all the prayers been for if God would not listen?

And behind it all was also a gnawing sense of guilt. He kept seeing his mother's face, gray and drawn, and when he looked at her he heard her words again: "You killed him, Joseph."

Many of the Saints came to visit in the next few days. Sister Slade came and stayed; she helped clean and cook, and she made Mother rest. The brethren from the Colesville settlement came and dug a grave near the bluffs along the edge of the oak forest. The next day Newel Knight gave a sermon at the service held beside the grave. The leaders of the settlements came from all over Clay County. William Phelps, the Whitmer brothers, Bishop Partridge, and all the other leaders from the Jackson County days were there. One after the other, all these men, and all of their wives, took occasion to talk to Joseph and the other children. They promised help, said that the boys should not worry. The brethren would raise a house for them; the women would help Mother. And they should trust in the Lord, who would give them strength to go on. Joseph never expressed any of his actual feelings. He thanked the people, just audibly, and he accepted their strong handshakes, but as he listened to them say essentially the same words over and over he sometimes wanted to run and hide in the woods just to stop the repetition.

Newel Knight said in his sermon that through the prophets man could sometimes glimpse into God's purposes, but that often we were simply not given knowledge to explain God's will. "It is not easy," he said, "to have to say farewell to Matthew Williams for now. But he is not the only one who has been called home. Several of the brothers who marched all the way from Ohio to help us have fallen to the cholera, and many more are gravely ill this day. This morning we were all deeply saddened to learn that our own dear Sidney Gilbert was also taken by the same disease. Only last week I shook Brother Gilbert's hand—that strong hand—and now he is gone from us. Brothers, sisters, it is at times like these that I am happy that I understand the Lord's plan for salvation. I know— we all know—that our friends live on in a better world."

Joseph had not known about Sidney Gilbert. Joseph knew how much Brother Gilbert had lost—his store in Jackson County and the modest wealth he had worked so hard to acquire. And now his life. Even *he* could be taken, who had given so much for the building of Zion. How many more would die?

Brother Knight continued, standing at the foot of the grave with the members gathered on slightly lower ground, in a half circle before him. "Perhaps these Saints had missions to perform on the other side of the veil. We cannot see there to know. But what we do know is that they died as martyrs to the great cause of building Zion. In every age there have been martyrs to the Lord's great works. And these martyrs have always lived on in the minds of later generations as witnesses to those works. Brother Matthew Williams will be remembered in this way. He was one of the stalwarts, always willing to serve."

Joseph cared little about the words that Brother

Knight spoke, but he listened. Brother Knight talked about death as a blessing, not a punishment, and then he concluded: "One thing we must trust in, brothers and sisters—God has not abandoned us. We have been tested and chastened, and the weak have turned their backs on the Lord, separated themselves from his church. But those who remain will yet triumph. With God as my witness, I promise that Zion will be established and the word will go forth to all the world. And Christ will return—the time is not far off—and he will reign upon this earth, and the earth shall be cleansed. Matthew Williams will come forth in the first resurrection, and he will fold his beloved family in his arms. And he will dwell with them forever. I bear testimony that it is so, brothers and sisters—even so, in Christ's holy name. Amen."

The Saints gave a resounding "amen" that echoed as a single, deep voice from the bluffs beyond the grave. Then Bishop Partridge said a prayer of dedication over the grave, and the wooden box was lowered with ropes by six of the men from the Colesville settlement.

Afterwards, everyone went back to the Williamses' cabin. Food had been brought, and many of the people, especially those from the Colesville branch, stayed for some time. Most everyone wanted to have a turn at reassuring Joseph again. Perhaps they sensed some cynicism in his aloofness. Matthew accepted the condolences and affirmed them, but Joseph only nodded. The words were still the same; there *were* no other words.

Joseph watched his mother. She had accepted it now, in her way. Joseph knew there would be no more screaming, no more desperate cries, not even any spoken suggestion that she doubted herself or God. But she would go inside herself; Joseph had seen it before. She had already turned inward, and her exterior looked blank as stone. She would work hard, say little, and she would ache, but she would not be able to touch anyone, not with tenderness. Joseph saw it all with dread. Where would he find anything to be happy about, to laugh at? There would be work

76

and loneliness, hopelessness and sameness. And it was all unfair. The only solace was to detest it all.

The Saints went home that afternoon, all but Sister Slade. Joseph slept soundly that night, and long; he could hardly come back to life the next day. Matthew went to work in the fields in the morning, but Joseph did not, and Matthew said nothing to him about it. Joseph walked the mile or so to the river, where he sat under a young cottonwood tree and stared at the muddy water. He watched for driftwood, and when he saw any, he let his eyes follow it along until it passed out of sight—but he did not think. Or at least he tried not to. It crossed his mind that this was the river that he and Matthew had crossed when they were finally safe, and he remembered that he had once stood on the other side with Joseph Smith and tried to throw a stone to Clay County. In coming weeks he would come to smirk at that memory, make light of the stupidity of such an attempt, but now he shoved the thought away and watched for driftwood. He wished that a riverboat would come by, but none did.

The next day Joseph returned to the same spot, sat in the same place. And the day after that he did the same. Each morning he only said, "I'm walking down to the river." He did not return to eat at noon; he only came back late in the day. Sister Slade's little girl stayed there to play with Ruth, and Ruth showed little awareness of Father's death. "Papa's in heaven," she said to Joseph. Joseph nodded. That was all. Joseph heard Sister Slade comment to her husband when he came by that Sister Williams had lost her milk. Brother Slade came back later with cow's milk. Samuel was still a weak-looking child, and a strangely quiet one who seemed to accept misery as part of his lot.

Mother was still sleeping a great deal. Some of her color was coming back, however, and Joseph could see that she was summoning her strength to go back to work. Joseph knew he had to do the same. Something within him said that no matter what he felt, he could not continue to let Matthew carry the whole load. But on the morning Sister Slade left, Joseph told Matthew he was going to the river again.

"No, Joseph," Matthew said.

Joseph stopped at the door and turned around. He was almost relieved to be stopped, but he could not bring himself to say so. "Why not?" he said.

"I need you here. We have a great deal of work to do. Mother needs help with the fire and in the house. Ruth needs some help, and the garden needs work. We must catch up now so we can get started on a house. We promised Father."

"*You* promised Father."

Matthew took two quick steps toward Joseph and grabbed him by the shoulder. "And you will help me keep that promise," he said, sternly but not stridently. "Mother will have her house. We will go on now and do the things that Father would have done. You have had enough time for tears; now we need to get back to work."

"I haven't been crying," Joseph said.

"Maybe you should then, Joseph. You need to get this over with. Father is gone now and that is that. Now we need to do what must be done. You are needed more than ever before. You're twelve now. You can't be a little boy any longer. It's time to start showing some signs of manhood."

Matthew sounded exactly like Father. His voice, the words he chose, even the way he stood, were a painful reminder to Joseph. Joseph felt a strange mixture of attitudes toward Matthew, feelings he didn't understand. "I'll work," Joseph finally said. "Just tell me what you expect me to do."

"That's fine. But it's more than that, Joseph. You have to settle this thing. There are things we have to accept. Everyone dies—*everyone*, Joseph. And it's not a bad thing to die. *We* understand that. Father's time came. We can't sit down now and feel sorry for ourselves."

Mother had been listening, across the room. "Matthew,

78

he needs some time," she said. Her voice was not tender, but she was attempting to bridge a gap. Joseph felt it, and he appreciated it. He longed to go to her.

"No, Mother," Matthew said, "I think not. It's not really a matter of time. At least not the part I'm talking about. We will all miss Father, and that can only change somewhat with time—but Joseph has to stop going to the river. He needs to get himself going again. I'll send him to school this fall, and he'll go on in that way too. But right now he needs to do some work, and he needs to take some satisfaction in doing the right things. For now, we all need to find our joy in our work."

"Joy?" Joseph shot back.

"Yes, Joseph, joy. If nothing else, say to yourself, 'I'm doing what Father would want me to do.' I'm afraid you have always struggled to find satisfaction in that."

"Matthew!" Mother said. "That's enough. Don't push so hard."

"Mother, I have to disagree with you. We all have to push very hard right now. We have no time to waste. We have more work to do than we have ever had before. I'm glad to see you going back to your own work today. Joseph can do the same."

Joseph and his mother looked at each other. Joseph knew she felt some solace in Matthew's strength, that she needed that kind of support, even direction. Joseph also knew, however, that she was struggling inside, that she would have preferred to be weak. He wanted to talk to her. There were things that needed to be said, but he couldn't bring himself to say them, nor could she, and he knew it. He would like to have been wrapped in her soft arms, but she was not soft now, and she couldn't help it, and he could not move toward her to help her break through the hardness.

Matthew was standing in the middle of the room, his feet set firm, in Father's accustomed position. His legs were powerful, thick as corner posts. He was a man now, Joseph saw. Matthew was not yet fifteen, but he was a man, partly because of who he was and partly because of who he had to be. In the shadowed light he looked like Father. He was almost as tall and he had the thick black hair. His face was still soft and he had no beard, but the arms, the shoulders, the thick neck—they were all Father's. Joseph sensed a kind of justice in that, but he ignored it. What he felt for the moment was resentment for Matthew's manner. Who was he to tell Mother what needed to be done? Who was he to be giving orders?

Joseph chopped wood that day, and he built a fire outside, to keep the cabin from heating up. He hoed weeds in the garden. And in the evening he read a book to Ruth and Samuel. It was a book that Sister Slade had brought, a collection of animal stories. He read the first one and then the second, and when Ruth pleaded with him to read more, he read a third. And that night he went to bed tired and, in some ways, relieved.

Chapter 10

After the tension of the impending war and the intense emotion brought on by the cholera epidemic, things calmed rather quickly for the Mormons in Clay County. The cholera stopped as suddenly as it had begun. Fourteen had died: twelve of the men from Zion's Camp, Sidney Gilbert, and Betsey Parrish, who had traveled in the camp with her husband. Joseph Smith released the men of the army, and in smaller groups they began to set out on the long march back to Ohio. The Prophet had made one attempt to negotiate the purchase of lands in Jackson County by offering to buy the lands of only those old settlers who felt they could not live in the same county with the Saints. But the old settlers were not interested, especially since Joseph Smith demanded compensation for property damage to Mormon homes and buildings.

The Saints were disappointed. They had been apprehensive about a possible war, but on the other hand, they had imagined the glory and joy of the triumphant return to Zion, led by their prophet. Now they had little hope of returning, at least in the near future. Joseph Smith stayed in the county for a few more days and directed the Clay County Saints in organizing their leadership into a high council and a presidency. David Whitmer was chosen to preside over the Church in Missouri. Soon after establishing the new leadership, the Prophet returned to Ohio, and the Saints began the process of establishing themselves more firmly in Clay County. They had to build better homes before the winter, and they had to make arrangements to rent or buy land. Zion would still be established, they believed, but for now they had to think simply of survival.

The summer continued very hot and humid and the grasshoppers were plentiful, but the crops were not bad that year. Many of the Mormons continued to struggle with their health, however. The towns along the river seemed to be plagued by one fever after another, and many of the Saints had never really recovered from the ordeal they had gone through the fall and winter before. In September Sally Knight, Newel's wife, gave birth to a baby boy who soon died. A few days later Sally died as well. She had struggled to survive for almost a year, but she was a frail woman, and her health had been broken by exposure to the cold and wet during the time of the expulsion. A few weeks after his wife's death, Newel was called to Ohio to preach the gospel along the way and then to work on the temple that was being built in Kirtland. Others of the Missouri leaders—David Whitmer, Parley Pratt, Lyman Wight, William Phelps, Bishop Partridge— were similarly called to such missions. For the Missouri Saints, it seemed that the center of their church was returning to Ohio, that the Missouri Mormons were now only hanging on for the future. And so these were days of difficulty and of disappointment.

Joseph's life, however, was not much influenced by the general movement of the Church. The initial sting of his father's death was gradually changing to a dull ache. He tried not to think about Father, tried just to deal with each day, but virtually every day something would cause him suddenly to feel the sharp sense of absence. Mostly he wanted to talk to Father, even if it were just one more time. There were simply things that needed one more thorough discussion. Joseph knew that, and yet he could not have verbalized exactly what those things were.

Joseph also found that he could not talk to Matthew any more. A stiffness had developed in their relationship. Matthew was careful with Joseph, kind but firm. He made Joseph work, told him what to do. Joseph never even

82

thought to complain, but he did not like the bossing. He did what he was told, never vigorously, but steadily and effectively enough.

Mother had remained silent—at least about her feelings—but she had taken on more resolve. Each day seemed a chore to her, but she never said that it was. She symbolized for Joseph what seemed to be the meaninglessness of their existence. All was routine. Everything she did seemed motivated by a desire to get the business of the day over with in preparation for the day to follow.

Ruth and Samuel suffered under the emotionless care. They were listless and cranky. There was no playfulness in them, or in any of the family.

The brethren from the Church came often, lent their support, gave Matthew advice, and the sisters came to visit Mother. But visitors seemed to leave saddened, as though the power of the family's mood was stronger than the one the visitors tried to bring.

Matthew found time to fell a few white oaks during the summer, but the work in the fields kept him from making much headway toward building the new house. However, a whole party of the Colesville Saints came over to help with the harvest. They picked the corn and then held a husking bee. A friendly competition was set up between two groups, each with a huge stack of corn to husk. The corn flew into the crib all day and by evening a job that would have taken the Williamses weeks was finished in a matter of hours. The Saints also promised to come back and help when the cabin was ready to be raised.

Matthew, with Joseph's help, then set about the serious business of building a home. They felled trees and stripped them of their limbs and then hewed the logs square. They were inexperienced, but Matthew had observed well and he soon became very proficient at the work. Joseph did as he was told. The two boys put in long days—as long as the light lasted every day, except for the Sabbath, of course. And Joseph could see that it was all Matthew could do to take that one day off. On Sunday afternoons he would take walks in the woods, where Joseph knew that he was actually choosing oaks that were the right size to cut.

The house was Matthew's great purpose—his promise to Father. But he never expressed to Joseph how he felt about it. Joseph could see that Matthew had a big cabin in mind, with more than one room, but he never asked Matthew what it would be like. Somehow Joseph knew that Matthew did not want to describe it, that he did not want to make any claims that he feared he could not produce. Perhaps if they could have talked and planned together, something would have happened inside Joseph. But as it was, Joseph was a mere laborer working for Matthew, and the house represented only endless work.

Some of the brethren came at times and helped with preparing the logs, and then one day early in October most of the Colesville men came and raised the new house. Others came back for days after until the split oak shingles were on, the shutters and door were hung, and the fireplace was completed. It was a large cabin, one of the nicest in the settlements in Clay County. Father had once told Matthew what he had in mind and Matthew had set out to complete the cabin according to those plans. Instead of the usual twelve-by-sixteen cabin, Matthew had constructed two rooms, the second only a little smaller than the first. It was bigger than necessary, but no one ever said so; everyone knew why Matthew had planned it as he had.

When the beds and other few pieces of furniture were carried in, Mother stood looking at it all. When Matthew came in she said, "Oh, son, it's so nice. I'm so proud of you."

"It'll be better yet, Mother. In the morning I plan to start cutting and splitting logs for a floor. And in the spring I'll take work for enough days to get cash for glass windows. Then I plan to make the shed over for a nice little barn. We'll have a cow and a team of mules or maybe a yoke of oxen—maybe both. And from what we get from our crop we'll start to pay Colonel Allen for this land. It will be ours before too many years."

Mother didn't exactly hug Matthew, but she put her arm around his shoulder. Neither cried. Neither could. But they were beginning to heal. Joseph stood in the door and watched. For the moment, he longed to share in the pride and happiness. But there was too much left unsettled in himself. He was almost angry at Matthew, who had so much purpose and who was now so close to Mother.

As fall came on, Joseph noticed the Saints' spirits rising. The end of the sickening heat and the coming forth of the splendor of the autumn forests was invigorating. He also noticed a new tendency among the Saints to speak less of Zion in Jackson County and to thank the Lord for the good land they lived upon now. Most had built new log cabins, and some had purchased the land they were living on. Everyone spoke of the rich soil, the good harvest, the ease with which good crops were produced. Farming was so much easier in the rich river valley than it had been in the rocky soil of the East, even better than in Jackson County, some felt. Not only that, but venison was readily available, as were turkey and rabbit and squirrel, ducks and geese. Honey was easily found or bought for next to nothing. Nuts and berries of all kinds grew wild in the woods; fruit trees thrived. It was simply a good place to live.

Joseph heard one of the brothers at church one day telling another man, "I suppose the center place will be over in Jackson County eventually, but I don't think everyone will live over there. I figure this is part of Zion too, and I plan to stay right here. I'm going to buy the farm I've been renting. I have me a good house now and the richest soil I ever seen. And not only that, I like these gentile folks over here on this side of the river. They're better folks to live around."

As the Saints' spirits rose, the sense of disappointment began to slip away. In the Colesville Branch, the new faith in the future was expressed with a new church building. It was a log structure, whitewashed outside and papered inside. It was the only whitewashed church in Clay County and the Saints were proud of it.

And yet, for Joseph not much had changed. He laughed sometimes, and outwardly he seemed much the same as he had before his father's death. He'd sometimes go to the woods with the Peck boys and swing in the grapevines that hung in the trees. Or he would gather walnuts and hickory nuts with his mother. At such times he seemed to forget to be unhappy. But as soon as he was alone for more than a few minutes, his spirits dropped. And Joseph was often alone. He was alone when he was with Matthew, and he was usually alone when he was with Mother.

A school had been established that fall. Matthew said that Joseph must go. Mother wanted Matthew to go as well, but Matthew said that the schooling he had was adequate. It was Joseph who needed learning, because of his mission. In a way, that was fine with Joseph. School was a haven from all the work that Matthew gave him to do, and it was a place to get lost in words and numbers. Joseph was a better student that winter than he had ever been before. It was not that he worked all that diligently, or even cared much, but he played less, talked less with his friends. Most of all, he loved to read, even if it was the scriptures. He read the Book of Mormon for its stories about Indians and wars, and he liked many of the stories in the Old Testament. He knew the answers to theological questions, enough to satisfy a teacher, but church principles did not really concern him. Joseph had reached a compromise with himself: he would not think about God, about death, about heaven, about faith, about truth. He had no answers—no personal answers—and he decided not to seek any. It was much easier that way.

The winter passed away quietly. When bad storms came, Joseph stayed home and Matthew directed his studies, just as Father had always done. At school, when the Peck boys teased the girls or went outside and wrestled, Joseph would join in sometimes, but afterwards he wondered why he had bothered to do it. He didn't care about any of that.

When spring began to break, Joseph often took the

86

long way home, walking down along the river. At school he could hear the cracking and booming as the ice began to break up. He liked to watch the ice flow, but what he looked forward to most was clear water and the return of the riverboats. The one thing that could still excite Joseph was the sound of the cannon blast signaling that a riverboat was about to put in at Liberty Landing. People from all over the southern part of the county and from Liberty itself would drop everything and head for the landing. The mood there was festive. The local people gathered around and called out and waved to the passengers, and the deck hands lowered the ramp and let the passengers get off. All sorts of people traveled on the riverboats; eastern ladies and gentlemen were side by side with backwoods trappers and hunters. Joseph had never seen a circus, but for him, this was that kind of show.

If a boat came in on a Saturday, Matthew would usually let Joseph go to the landing to watch it dock. Matthew knew it was Joseph's one real pleasure. He always said, "But be back in an hour—hour and a half at the most." He never said anything if Joseph were actually gone longer, yet Matthew didn't like Joseph's going and Joseph knew it. Matthew hated to break up his scheduled day and he hated the waste of time, but mostly he feared the wicked influence of the gentiles who spilled out onto the landing from the decks of the riverboats.

It was not the wickedness that attracted Joseph. He heard the cursing, saw the gamblers and the rough old roustabouts, but all that meant nothing to him. What he liked were the beautiful boats themselves, the fancy white gingerbread decorations, the tall black smokestacks. He always imagined himself as a pilot, in control of the big vessels, seemingly in control of the river itself. There was a great respect among river people for the pilots. Most of the stories that Joseph heard the deck hands tell were about some wise old pilot and how he had outwitted the river. Joseph knew that Matthew would not like the idea, and he knew his father had been opposed, but Joseph wanted to be a riverboat pilot. He wanted to be in command of the river, to travel up and down the Missouri and the Mississippi, and he wanted the boys along the rivers to look at him with envy and admiration.

One day in April, when school was about to close, Joseph was nearing home when he heard someone back in the woods whistle. He stopped and looked and saw Ollie leaning against a tree. "Is that you, Ollie?"

" 'Course it is. Who'd you think?" he said, and he laughed.

Joseph felt a joy surge in him that he hadn't felt for a year. He ran to Ollie and the two shook hands, awkwardly, neither knowing exactly how to express their friendship.

"What are you doing, Ollie?"

"We just put in about two hours ago at the landing. We're off again in the morning first thing. I'm took on as a cub now. I'm learning the river."

"A cub pilot? You mean you'll be a pilot someday?"

"Yup."

"Ollie, that's wonderful. It's what *I* want."

"You wanna go on the river?" Ollie looked doubtful.

"Yes, I do," Joseph said, but he wanted none of Ollie's advice to avoid the river, which was surely coming, so he changed the subject. "I thought I would never see you again. I always asked about you at the landing, but no one ever said he knew you or had seen you."

"Well, I seen Mr. Allen and he told me you was always asking about a feller named Ollie. 'Course, I asked him about you, and that's how he knowed who I was. He told me your pa died and all. So I just figured I'd stop over and say hello to you."

"Sure. Come on to the house and have supper."

"No. I think I better not, Joseph. I gotta git back directly, and I don't think I'm wanted at your place."

"But Father is—"

"I know, but I suspect Matthew and your ma would just as leave not see me no more."

88

"What do you mean? You saved Matthew's life."

"You done most of that, Joseph. Maybe some other time I'll stop by and see Matthew, but I'm not sure I should. I'm just a river man now, and not fit company for a Mormon boy." Ollie had not apparently meant to tease Joseph nor hurt him. He seemed to mean what he said, and Joseph understood that.

"Well, I guess I ain't such a good Mormon boy, Ollie."

Ollie laughed. "You wouldn't make it on the river, Joseph. You still cain't say 'ain't' and make it sound right."

Joseph laughed at himself. "I guess I can learn," he said. "I want to be a pilot more than anything."

"Why?"

"What do you mean? Why are *you* learning it?"

"I don't know. I guess 'cause it's 'bout the best job on the river—if you *gotta* be on the river. But it ain't no good way to live, Joseph. I don't know nobody but filthy old deck hands and riverboat engineers. And I us'ly don't know them for long. You spend all day ever' day just hearing that old steam engine choking like it's about to drown and listening to an old pilot holler at you what an empty-head you are."

"But once you get to be a pilot, just think what you will be."

"What will I be, Joseph?"

"Everyone will look up to you. You'll be in control, Ollie, and everyone will know it."

"But it's not like you think, Joseph. It's still just looking at the same old muddy river all day, and getting on sand-bars and ketching snags, and always wondering if the old boiler won't bust one day and scald you to death."

But Joseph's mind wasn't changed; he assumed that Ollie was making it sound as bad as possible because he didn't want to be blamed for leading Joseph away from home.

"How you getting on since your pa died?"

"Well enough, I guess."

"Matthew has taken over, has he?"

"That's exactly what he's done. He bosses me around like he thinks he's my father."

"Did he build the house?"

"He thinks he did. But lots of people helped, and I was one of them."

"Do you still miss your pa?"

Joseph's glance dropped toward the ground. "Yeah, I miss him."

"Well, I sorta know the troubles. I ain't exactly had a pa either, since he told me to get out. But then I guess I was a little older and it was different in some ways."

Ollie and Joseph talked for a while longer, but Ollie couldn't stay. He said he expected to be back up the Missouri often now, unless his company put him on a different line, which was always possible. And so Ollie was gone again; once again he had slipped in and out of Joseph's life as uncontrollably as a summer storm.

Chapter 11

Not long after school was out Matthew told Joseph one night that they needed seed corn and some tools, so he was going into Liberty the next day and wanted Joseph to go along. Joseph knew that he was not really needed, that this was Matthew's way of giving Joseph a day off from working—or at least part of one. The boys left fairly early the next morning. They took the wagon that Matthew had been reconstructing from the broken old carcass of a wagon that had been left on the farm.

They had barely gotten underway when Matthew said, "Joseph, I've been wanting to talk to you." He waited but Joseph only watched old Sally's haunches and said nothing. "You don't seem to be coming back from this thing very well. You don't seem happy. Are you still missing Father?"

"Yes." It wasn't the whole answer, or any sort of explanation, but Joseph did not really have one, so he let Matthew's suggestion stand.

"I understand that, Joseph. I miss him too. It's hard for me because I have so many questions I would like to ask him about the farm all the time. But we have to go on without him, Joseph. You can't spend your life looking back. You have to just say that what is over is over."

Joseph did not say anything. He had heard all this before, knew the speech by heart, even knew it was true, but it didn't seem to change the way he felt.

"Joseph, I'm not saying this whole thing the way I want to. It's not easy for me to try to take over and do some of the things Father would do. I'm not Father, and I don't want you to think that I am pretending that I am. But somebody has to try to get you out of this."

In a way, Joseph wanted to respond. He did like the tone that Matthew was taking; he knew Matthew meant well. But there was an emptiness in Joseph. There was simply nothing to say.

"I guess one of the things I want you to know is that you did *not* kill Father. When Mother said that, she was tired and upset. She didn't really mean it then, and she doesn't think so now. Do you understand that?"

"Yes." Joseph only answered this way to avoid the discussion that would follow if he told the truth. She *had* meant it. Maybe she did not think so any more, or maybe she was sorry she had said it, but at the time she had been completely serious. She had not said it on sudden impulse; it had come out of her only after much thought. And she had never taken it back. Joseph didn't know whether he had killed his father, but he knew that he had never settled the matter with his mother. It was not something that Matthew could do for her.

"But are you still holding on to that worry? Is that what's bothering you?"

Joseph couldn't bring himself to answer. If he had said yes, that would not really be the answer exactly, and no was just as wrong. It was complicated in some way that Joseph did not understand himself. If he said anything at all he would then have to discuss the whole thing, try to pull the answers out of himself, and above all, Joseph did not want to do that.

"Joseph, you can't just keep holding all this inside you. You aren't even Joseph anymore. If you could try to talk to me or to Mother, I think it would help. It's what you need."

Joseph closed in tight and held on. If he could resist now, he could keep his silence. Matthew clucked at the mule and fell silent himself. Nothing more was said until they reached Liberty. And then Matthew finally said, with an edge of frustration, maybe even a little anger, "I don't

92

know what else I can say to you, Joseph. You won't talk to me. But you need to do something. I want to see you go on and do something with your life. You still have big things ahead. You are the one in the family who has been singled out to serve."

Joseph's face popped around with an angry stare, and the boys looked at each other knowingly. "All right, Joseph. If that's how you want it, you throw away your mission and everything else. But I plan to do the things Father asked me to do. I *promised.* I would think you'd want to take his advice, at least now—you never would when he was alive."

Now Joseph was glad he had not opened up to Matthew. It was still there: the old complaint against him. Matthew still felt the same way.

Matthew stopped Sally in front of the supply store and got down from the wagon. Joseph stayed where he was. He liked to look about the town square and the stores that lined it. Right now it was a way to avoid thinking. Liberty was a nicer town than Independence. It was somewhat bigger and it had a neater appearance. It was perhaps a little like the town Joseph had always imagined as the center of Zion. Or at least it was the closest thing Joseph had seen on the frontier to a town that was worthy of such a purpose. A man came along the path in front of the stores. He nodded to Joseph. "How do," he said.

Joseph nodded to him. There were other people passing in and out of the stores or blacksmith shops, or driving by in wagons. Joseph liked it all; his spirits rose amazingly. It struck him how much he missed by always being alone on the farm. He needed change; he needed activity.

Before long another man came along the dirt path in front of the store. He had on a black suit and a bowler hat. Joseph nodded to the man and said, "Hello."

"Are you saved, young man?" the man asked. He stopped and gave Joseph a long, hard stare.

Joseph was rather amused, but he was not about to answer. He simply looked away.

"What'sa matter, boy? Cain't you look me in the eye? Is it the sin in your heart that makes you turn your head that way? Are you saved or ain't you, boy? I want to know."

Joseph found himself smiling. The man was serious— there was no doubt about that—and yet his exaggerated manner of speech and his passionate intensity made him ridiculous to Joseph.

"So you think it's funny, do you, boy? When you burn in hell you won't find so much to laugh about. You better change your evil heart and change it now—you better get yourself saved. Now give me an answer. Are you saved or ain't you?" When Joseph didn't answer again the man stepped closer to the wagon. "Did you hear me, boy? You better answer, because God is listening. Are you saved?"

"I just want to be saved from the likes of you," Joseph said. He had to laugh at his own response; it felt good. And then he heard another man laughing. It was one of the men who worked in the store, a broad-bellied man with a jean apron on.

"I guess he answered you, Seth," the big man said.

"You'll both burn in hell for laughing about the Lord's holy truths," the preacher responded, not a single sign of laughter in his own face. "Neither of you is saved, that's for sure, and both of you will find yourself in the fires of hell in payment for your sins."

"I may do that, but this boy won't. He's a good Mormon boy. Old Joe Smith is taking the whole bunch with him straight into the everlasting glory."

"A Mormon, is he? I should of knowed. A boy with no more respect than that—I should of knowed. Ain't none of the Mormons that respect the law or anything else. They'd just as leave kill you and take your land and then say God told 'em it was no more'n right."

"That's right, mister," Joseph said. "And I'm thinking right now about killing you. Have you got any land?"

There was a great burst of laughter from the man in

the door, as well as from two men who had come up behind the wagon without Joseph realizing it.

"You see," the preacher shouted. "There's a witness. He has no more respect than to make a joke of killing and murdering and thieving. These are the very abominations of which his own people is guilty. Do you deny it, boy?"

Joseph thought he had said enough. A man and his boy had crossed the street from the town square to see what was going on, and another man had come down the pathway and had stopped to listen.

"Do you deny it or don't you? Your own silence is a witness against your people. Are the Mormons murderers and thieves?"

"They aren't, but I might be doing some murdering if you don't leave me alone." Joseph knew he was being feisty and he enjoyed it. This was not the sort of thing a good Mormon boy would do, but Joseph found himself not caring much about that. And the men who were listening were laughing boisterously. Joseph felt like jumping down and poking the preacher in the eye. It made him feel alive again just to think about it.

"You heard him," Seth shouted. "He's a witness against himself, and God is recording ever' word on his tablets at this very moment."

"I hope he puts down what a fool it was I was talking to," Joseph said. He didn't say it loud, but loud enough for all to hear. He found some pleasure in having an audience. A man and his wife came across the street to see what was happening.

"What's going on?" someone said.

The big man from the store said, "It's a Mormon boy taking on old Seth Pingree. And he's giving him all the 'what for' Seth can handle, too."

Joseph felt rather foolish after that remark, and he also sensed that he was running out of retorts. Yet he hardly knew how to get out of his predicament. Not only that, the preacher was not about to stop until he got a last word in.

"I say unto all this people," Seth began, and it was clear that an oration was about to come forth, "I say that Joe Smith is a tool of the devil hisself, a filthy deceiver with a lying tongue and a black heart. He has misled this poor boy into such disrespect for the Lord's anointed witnesses. I forgive this poor child because it ain't really his own fault. He's been misguided—sadly misguided."

"Then what's your excuse, mister?" Joseph said. Everyone laughed, and Joseph saw one man slap another on the back while both of them shook their heads and looked at each other with obvious enjoyment.

Someone yelled, "Yeah, Seth, who got you all turned around backwards?"

Suddenly Joseph heard Matthew. "That's enough, Joseph." Matthew pushed past the big man in the door. "That's enough foolishness. Show more respect for your own people." He said it only to Joseph, but everyone was close enough to hear.

"Seth must be right," a man said. "I guess that boy *don't* have no respect."

"That's enough," Matthew said to the people. "I need to load some corn here." He returned to the store, but he was soon back with a sack of corn on his shoulder. He dropped it on the back of the wagon, and the old springs squeaked and dust flew up. "Come on, Joseph, give me a hand with some of these other things." Joseph jumped down and went into the store. When the boys came back to the wagon people had begun to walk away, but Seth was not about to let it all end that easily.

"You'll be driven out of this county soon," he said, not as loudly as before, nor with so much flair, but with equal intensity. "I hope you know it's true. Our people let you come in here 'cause you was hungry and cold. We done the Christian thing. But now you are polluting our—"

"Leave the boys alone," the big man said. "Why don't you go along now, Seth."

"I *said*," and he raised his voice again, "I said you was a pollution. And you must be kept off from good Christian

96

folk. You ain't gonna last here in Clay, so there's no use putting in more corn. You better find a place away from here or you'll regret that you didn't."

Matthew got up on the wagon and Joseph climbed in behind him. They tried to ignore Seth, but he continued.

"People is talking now. They're saying they never 'spected you to stay here and they allus told you it was just till you could get ready to move on again. They want you out. Now that's true. Even Mr. Bowen here will tell you so. Ain't it true, Bowen?"

The man in the door said, "Seth, I told you to move on."

"But it's true, ain't it? You tell 'em."

Both boys now looked at Mr. Bowen. "Boys, there's some that feels the way he says. I suppose you know that. But as far as I'm concerned you can do business with me anytime—and that goes for all the Mormons. They all seem to be real fine folks."

"That's fine for you, Bowen, but you'd sell your soul for a dollar."

"Maybe a dollar and six bits, Seth," Bowen said, laughing, his whole frame jiggling. "I don't sell cheap."

"That's right. You make light of all this. All the same, the good Christian folks is getting organized, and if these Mormons don't move out of here, they'll think what they got in Jackson was a picnic."

"What do you have in mind, Seth? A church social?"

"That's all right, Bowen. These boys will see. I'm telling 'em not to put in that corn, to save it for some other field to plow some other place."

Matthew clucked at Sally and flipped the reins. Sally stepped ahead and then Matthew turned her around.

"Now boys," Seth shouted, "don't misunderstand. I love *all* God's children. I don't blame you. I know you've been misguided by that lying Joe Smith."

Matthew glanced at Joseph. "Then what's his excuse?" Matthew said. Both boys laughed. Joseph laughed more than he had in at least a year.

Chapter 12

It was good for Matthew and Joseph to laugh together again. Joseph was reminded of the days when he could easily break through Matthew's seriousness. And it was good to know that Matthew could still see humor in things —in anything. But Matthew returned home to work, and work he did. Joseph, of course, worked hard too, but never with Matthew's sense of purpose. Joseph felt a bit more at ease with Matthew after that day. The two boys came to a sort of compromise: they never discussed Joseph's feelings, his deeper motivations, not even his future. They lived side by side on rather friendly terms, but there was a reserve between them that persisted.

Joseph could see that Mother was gradually yielding her hard exterior; her "better self" was returning in many ways. Joseph saw the effect this had on Ruth and Samuel, who seemed to flourish with Mother's returned affection and attention. In fact, Mother seemed to find renewed meaning in life by giving love to the two younger children. She was helped also by Matthew's devoted commitment to the fulfilling of all Father's plans. After the corn was in that spring, Matthew left Joseph to keep the squirrels out of the crop and to repair the fences and care for the garden, and he went to work at the slaughter yard. He worked for three weeks and was able to earn nine dollars. He bought a calf that he expected to raise into a good milk cow, and then he ordered the promised glass windows from St. Louis. He also promised Mother he'd get her a spinning wheel and a loom when the harvest came in.

Mother responded well to Matthew's accomplishments. She seemed relieved to know that she had not been left destitute by her husband's death. But of course her life was still not the same as it would have been. A sadness remained in her eyes, in her voice at times. Sometimes, even now, Joseph saw her holding Samuel on her lap, hugging him close, quietly crying. But she never hugged Joseph. He was thirteen now, and he would have resisted her affection, but then she never tried to embrace him either. She talked to Joseph about matters of daily life, about almost everything, but never about the things that mattered—not about religion, or death, or Father, or about how Joseph felt about all of these.

Joseph slipped away to the river when he could. Sometimes he tried to see how far out into the current he could throw a stone. He avoided thinking about the day he and Joseph Smith had thrown rocks into the Missouri; he simply wanted to test himself, and he felt some pride in his growing strength. Sometime in his life, he now believed, he would be a riverboat pilot. If Ollie had done it, so would he. And then he would control the boat and even the river. He would not have to worry about the width or power of the river, because he would ride the surface and the vastness would be nothing to the power he would control. Sometimes he stood by the water and pretended that he was at the wheel of his own boat. He could feel the impulses in his arms telling him exactly what to do, how to respond to the subtle tricks of the current, how to maneuver past all dangers. He was always victorious.

The Saints were beginning to prosper again, just as they eventually had in Jackson County. Some began to buy land. Lyman Wight set up a brickmaking operation and contracted to build a large brick home for Michael Arthur, a well-to-do Clay County man. Some worked in Liberty or in the hemp factory along the river. But most farmed the rich soil on rented farms and talked of the days when they would own the land they worked. Clay County had become the new Mormon center in the West, and most of the Saints felt satisfied to stay there. In the fall of 1835 word came from Kirtland that a build-up in Missouri was to take place. Some Mormons were migrating to Clay County already, and many more were to come in the spring. And there was even talk that perhaps another army would be mustered and Jackson County would be retaken after all.

But there were other signs that were less promising. What old Seth had claimed was actually true. Some of the old settlers in Clay County were growing tired of having the Mormons in their area. They had been willing to take in hungry, deprived people and help them to get food and shelter, but they had always expected the Mormons to either go back to Jackson County or move on to some other location.

Now that the Saints were beginning to buy farms and to talk of the pleasure they found in the lands they lived on, some of the old settlers began to feel concerned. Some of the Saints even spoke rather openly of Clay County as being a part of Zion, the land that the Mormons would someday take possession of with God's help. While many of the old settlers liked the Mormons, the old complaints began to be heard again: Mormons were fanatics, they said, odd people who believed and behaved differently from other Christians. Mormons were opposed to slavery and would help the slaves rise up against their masters. And the claim was also made that the Mormons planned to join with the Indians and drive out everyone who was not of their own faith.

But the greatest fear among the old settlers was in the numbers of Mormons and the way they gathered to one place. This gathering was strange behavior to the frontier people, and more than that, it gave the Mormons power, which was threatening.

And so there was talk again of troubles, of civil war. Most Mormons believed that the opposition was milder in Clay than in Jackson County, that there were more decent, level-headed people to control the extremists, and many of the Saints predicted that God would never again allow such mobs to drive away his people. But Joseph wondered about that. He felt no terror, no dread, as he had before, because he planned another future, separate from the Saints. All the same, he wondered how long it might be before the Jackson County pattern repeated itself. Father had predicted that it would.

In March of 1836 Joseph turned fourteen. He had grown during the winter. He was almost as tall as Matthew, even though Matthew was now sixteen. Joseph was all legs, however, and though he was strong, he was lean and light. Matthew, by contrast, was firm as an oak, with big shoulders. He was a handsome young man with his dark hair and eyes and his healthy-looking dark skin. But Joseph was always sunburnt, his nose peeling skin and his cheeks deeply red. His wild hair would lighten to almost white in the summer. Mother told him to wear a hat, but half the time he didn't, and the wind tossed his hair into tangles.

When school was out, Sister Betsey Knight, who was only nineteen, told Joseph he might as well not come back in the fall. She had given him all she knew how to teach. Matthew said there was a high school in Liberty and that he wanted Joseph to go to it the next fall, but Joseph concluded that he would not go. Of course, he said nothing of this to Matthew.

One day in May Ollie suddenly showed up again. Joseph had expected him all summer and fall the year before but had never seen him. As it turned out, Ollie had stopped at Liberty Landing a few times, but he had never come over to visit, and Joseph had never gone to the landing on the right days to see him. Ollie had been moved to a different boat, but he was still in training, not yet a full-fledged pilot.

Ollie showed up at the farm one evening and walked out to the field to greet Matthew as well as Joseph. "Nice to see you again, Ollie," Matthew said, and the two shook hands. "Can you stay for supper?" Joseph thought of Father.

"Naw, I just stopped to say hullo. I wasn't sure you'd like to see me."

"I'm happy to see you, Ollie," Matthew said, "and I'd like to have you share supper with us."

"I 'spose I could then," Ollie said. "Thanks."

But at supper Matthew found little to say to Ollie, and Joseph did not want to discuss his own questions in front of everyone. Mother was nice to Ollie, however, asking him about his life on the river.

"Do you ever get down as far as New Orleans?" Mother asked.

"A couple of times, I have."

"Is it as exciting as people say it is?"

"I don't get too far from off the docks us'ly, ma'am. I guess it's exciting all right, but not the kind of place a nice Mormon lady like yourself would like."

Mother blushed as deeply as Joseph had ever seen her blush. "Well, I suppose not," she said.

"I didn't mean to say—"

"No, that's fine, Ollie. I am certain you are right."

But Joseph sensed that his mother had longed to see some places in the world. He knew she had never liked the prairies, not even with Father, but especially without him. Suddenly Joseph wanted to escape more than he ever had before. He felt sorry for Mother. He did not want to end up with a life someone else had chosen for him, the way Mother had. Maybe he could leave now, with Ollie. He knew that Matthew could use his help on the farm, but Joseph could not tie himself to Matthew's life forever. Maybe the time had come to make the break, now that he was out of school. He felt excited by the possibility. The thoughts of another long summer in the fields in the Missouri heat had been weighing on Joseph, but this new idea pumped life back into him.

After supper Joseph and Ollie walked outside. "Ollie," Joseph said, "I have to talk to you. Do you think I could get a job on your riverboat?"

"Mine? Maybe. But not a kind of work you'd want.

102

They can sometimes use boys for kitchen help or for deck hands, but it's all work, and I mean hot work, too. You start early and never stop till the boat puts in, if it does. Sometimes with a good moon we keep right on going all night. And you never seen such men to work 'round. Most of 'em would just as soon kill you as say 'howdy.' "

"But couldn't I work up? Couldn't I get to be a cub pilot, like you did?"

"It's allus possible, but it ain't likely. I was mighty lucky, that's all."

"Well, I want to try my luck. Will you help me?"

"No, Joseph, I won't. Matthew and your ma needs you here. And it ain't no way for a religious boy to live."

"Well, maybe I'm not so religious as you think, Ollie. So don't let that worry you."

"I'm afeerd I don't believe that, Joseph. I think you'd be heading back this way about the first time we docked long enough to bring on firewood."

"Maybe not. Try me and see."

Ollie took a long look at Joseph. Ollie was getting to be a big man; he was not only taller than Joseph by a good bit, but he carried what seemed twice the bulk. His shoulders and his arms bespoke power and animal force, but there was still something childish in his manner, in his shyness, and in his pleasant eyes. "No, Joseph," he said softly. "I won't help you leave here. So don't ask me no more."

"Ollie, I'm going whether you help me or not." Joseph felt frustrated, almost angry. Now that he had gotten excited about leaving, he didn't want to face going back to the same life he had been struggling with since Father had died. Suddenly he turned and walked back into the house.

"Matthew, I've decided to take work on the river," he said. He stood before Matthew, but he did not really look him in the eyes. "It's what I've been wanting to do for a long time, and now that I'm out of school this is a good time to get started."

Matthew and Mother were standing near each other,

both having risen from the table just as Joseph had entered the door. They stared at Joseph as though they had not really understood what he had said. Some of Joseph's resolve slipped away, but he went on. "I'm just going to pack up a few of my things—my other clothes—and go now. I think that would be best."

"Joseph," Mother said, "whatever—"

"Now wait. Just a minute, Joseph," Matthew said, drowning out Mother's voice. "You are not just suddenly taking off like this. You are only just turned fourteen. Is this some idea of Ollie's?"

Ollie was at the door. "No, it ain't," he said. "I told Joseph it's the wrong thing for him. And I told him I warn't going to help him get a job neither. The whole thing was his own idea."

"That's easy enough to say, Ollie. But you come in here pumping him full of stories about the exciting life on the river. Where do you suppose he got the idea?"

"Not from me, Matthew. I told 'im the truth. There ain't nothing exciting about it. It's just plain old work. But I don't 'spect you to believe me, Matthew. You never did. I'll be leaving now. I wish I'd never come by; I said I wouldn't once before, and I should of just left it at that. 'Bye, Joseph. 'Bye, Mrs. Williams."

Ollie turned to go but Joseph said, "Wait, Ollie. I'm going with you. Matthew can't make me stay. He's not my father, even if he thinks he is, and it wouldn't matter anyway. I'm old enough to do what I want."

"Joseph," Mother said, "don't talk that way. Think of your father. What would he say?"

"I don't know, Mother—well, I guess I do. But I've got to think for myself now."

There was silence, and time seemed to stop for a moment. Then Ollie said, "Joseph, I won't help you get a job on the river. You better stay here where you belong." Joseph's anger was gone now, and when he watched his mother's eyes filling with tears, he felt himself giving way, but he was not quite ready to say so. It would make him a boy all over again to admit that he had to obey. If nothing else, he wanted to break from Matthew's authority.

But Matthew was obviously angry. "Joseph, you are not going anywhere. And Ollie, thank you for all you've done for us, but please don't come around any more. My father told you to leave once; I tell you now. I hope it won't have to be said again."

"It sure won't," Ollie said, and he left.

Joseph was angry again, angrier than before. "You had no right to do that, Matthew. He's my friend."

"Joseph, I am head of this household, and you have to accept that."

"You're only two years older than I am. You can't boss me around like some farmhand. I don't like farm work. I'm going to do what *I* want to do. I want to be a riverboat pilot, and that's what I am going to do."

"And what about your calling, Joseph?" Matthew had spread his feet and assumed his position of authority, his fatherly firmness. It was that same position Joseph had seen so many times before, his father's rock-wall steadiness. "What about your religion? Does it mean nothing to you?"

"I never was as religious as you, Matthew. You know that. You take my calling. I always told you it suited you better anyway."

"Is that what you would tell Joseph Smith? Is that what you would tell Father?"

Joseph did not answer. He went to the little crate in the back room where he kept his few possessions. He grabbed his extra breeches, two shirts, and some stockings and underwear. He rolled them together and then walked back to where Matthew was standing. Matthew was still set, his arms still folded, but now he stood directly in front of the door. Mother had picked up Samuel, who had begun to cry, and Ruth was clinging to Mother's leg. Ruth looked frightened and confused. Joseph only glanced at Mother and the little children, but he looked at Matthew directly. "I'm sorry to have to go this way, but I think it's best. But I *will* say to you, Matthew, that you make it easier to leave."

105

"Joseph, please," Mother said. "Couldn't you at least wait a day or two and let us have a chance to talk about all this? You and I have needed to talk; I've wanted . . ." Her voice caught and she couldn't continue. Joseph couldn't look at her.

Joseph might have stayed then. For a moment he tried to think of a face-saving way to back down. But then Matthew said, "That's right, Joseph. I want you to stay and talk things over. I won't have you just running off at a moment's notice."

"I *ain't* just running off, Matthew. I've considered it for a long time." He started toward the door and tried to step around Matthew. But Matthew moved in front of him. "If I have to fight you to get out of here, I will, Matthew. Maybe you can whip me and try to hold me here. But sooner or later I'll get my chance, and when I do I'm going. So you might as well move over and let me go."

"All right, Joseph, it's your choice." Matthew grabbed Joseph by the shoulders. "Now you look me in the eye and hear what I have to say, and then you give it some serious thought before you head out of here." The boys' faces were close together, and Joseph matched Matthew's steady stare. "If you step out that door, you have chosen Ollie's world—the gentile world. You have turned your back on your family, on your own people, and on your Father in heaven. And so if you step out that door, make it forever. Don't come back."

Mother gasped. "Oh, Matthew, don't say such a thing."

"That's an easy choice, Matthew," Joseph said, "I don't want your world." He stepped around Matthew and walked out the door.

Chapter 13

Joseph walked straight to the landing and to Ollie's riverboat, the *Roebuck*. He asked a man who was standing on the main deck whether Ollie had just come aboard, and the man, who turned out to be the first mate, said that he had and directed Joseph to Ollie's cabin. Ollie bunked in the texas above the promenade deck now that he was a cub pilot. Joseph climbed the stairs and knocked at the door that the first mate had pointed out.

"Joseph," Ollie said, when he opened the door. "I was afeerd of this. I ain't helping you—just like I told you. And I hope they don't have no jobs."

"Won't you even tell the captain I'm a good worker?" Joseph could see into the tiny room, and noticed that Ollie shared it with another man, since there were two bunks.

"Nope. I won't tell the captain anything. And don't use my name. Maybe you gotta find out for yourself, but I ain't gonna help you get into this kinda life. The best thing would be for you to hightail it back to your own place right now."

"I can't," Joseph said. "Matthew told me not to come back—ever."

"He was just mad at you. He'll take you back if you go back and say you're sorry and want to come home."

"I can't do that."

"Not yet, maybe."

"Not ever."

"We'll see, Joseph. Anyhow, I still ain't helping you. You'd hate me for't in a few days."

"All right, Ollie. Since no one will help me, I'll take

care of myself. It's just as well. I have to start doing that now anyway."

Joseph walked back down the stairs and found the first mate. "Are you the captain?" he said.

The first mate was a slender man with wide-flaring, "mutton chop" whiskers and a tooth missing in the front of his mouth. He was dressed in a dark blue suit of clothes with braid on the shoulders. The braid had once been gold, but it was now faded and dirty, as was the man himself.

"Well, I guess you could say I am, boy. At least until the captain hisself gits back from town. If you'd been about the river a bit, you'd know a first mate when you see one." This was all said with condescension and an air of importance.

Joseph wanted to say, "So don't you think you're something?" but he didn't. "Do you have any work I could get?" Joseph asked. "I'd take whatever you have."

"I guess you would. How old are you?"

"Sev . . . sixteen, almost seventeen."

"Do you work as bad as you lie?"

Joseph felt himself color. "I can work with any man," Joseph said, and he pulled himself up tall and looked the first mate in the eye.

"You can, can you?" He chuckled and ran his tongue across his chapped lips. "Ain't you something! There's men on this boat what could eat you for breakfast and pick your bones outa their teeth after they's through. We got men what been on the river three times longer than you been alive—men what can pick up a sleeping mule and set her down on the bank without waking her up."

"You don't lie so well yourself," Joseph said.

The man looked stunned for a moment and then Joseph smiled at him. The first mate let a grin spread across his thin lips. "Well, my oh my. You *are* a hot one. I might hire you on, just so I can have me a good laugh when you go off with your tail up in between your legs like a old coon dog what rousted out a sleeping bear."

108

"Give me a chance and I'll show you I can work," Joseph said.

"I just might give you a try. Can you handle a little heat, since you're such a hot one?"

"I've worked in the hot sun all my life."

"What's that—'leven, twelve years?" Joseph didn't answer, but he smiled at the first mate. "What I meant was a little more'n hot sun. We need a fireman. We us'ly don't use no little boys for work like that, but we need someone bad and we need him right now. Do you 'spose you could tend a fire and keep it fed and keep it burning high and powerful? And maybe do some chores for the engineer besides?"

"Sure. I could do that."

"How come you're so sure? You never even seen the job done before."

"Yes, I have. I was on the *Chieftain* awhile back. I watched what everyone did."

"You did, did you? Well, then, I guess you know all about it. I guess you'll be showing us what to do. I mean any boy what has already rode on a riverboat and watched a fireman—least any boy as hot as you—sure can say that he knows what is what."

Joseph refused to back down, refused to act humble. "I'll work hard at it," was all he said. "You'll see I can do it."

"Is Ollie a friend of yours?"

"No."

"Well, what is he?"

"I know him, that's all. Not too well."

"I see. He wouldn't speak for you. Is that what you're saying?"

"I'm just saying that I'll take the job. And if you find I can't do it, fine. You can let me go."

"I wonder if you know what you're saying. This little boat ain't got but one boiler, and one man has to keep that fire going all day—as long as we run. If we don't make good time, it's the fireman what gets the blame."

"I still say I can do it."

"You do, do you? Where you from, boy? Is your daddy out looking for you? Did you run off?"

"I'm from right here in Clay County. And my father is dead. I'm setting out on my own now."

"You don't talk like nobody from these parts."

"I lived in New York when I was a boy."

"And what are you now?" Joseph didn't answer. "My guess is, you're one of these Mormons what come out here from New York. Ain't that right?"

"Yes."

"Well, that's a good one. Just what we need. A eastern Mormon boy for a fireman. The captain would laugh till he fell right off this old boat if I was to tell him I hired a Mormon boy to tend our fire. Either that or he'd run me off for doing it."

"Don't tell him. I'm not a Mormon anymore. I'm on my own."

The mate chuckled again. "You're a hot one awright. I think I'll heat you up for a day or two and watch you melt."

"Where do I bunk?"

"I'll get to that. We cain't pay you much at all. Let's say your grub and a dollar a week. If you show some sticking power, we'll get you a little more'n that. How's that sound?"

"Fine." Joseph would have taken the job for nothing. What he wanted most was to get out of Clay County.

"Then you're on. My name's Henry Parkinson, *Mr.* Parkinson to you. You'll answer to Jack, the engineer, but since I'm hiring you, I'm gonna watch you close and make sure you don't make me look bad. If you cain't work I'll put you on the riverbank at the next landing. There ain't no work tonight, but if I was you I'd sleep hard and I'd get started now. 'Cause at four o'clock you'll be rousted out, and you won't see that bed again for eighteen hours, if you see it that soon."

Actually, all this did not sound very attractive to Jo-

110

seph, but he was too set on proving himself to allow any doubts. He would prove he was a man. Parkinson took Joseph inside to a dingy room crowded with ten or twelve bunks. A man in his long underwear was lying on his back in one bunk, sleeping wheezily but peacefully. Parkinson said that most of the men had gone into town. Joseph was given the last bunk in the corner, the one furthest from the door or any source of air.

Parkinson left and Joseph sat down on his bunk. The room was hot and the odor of the men who had been sleeping there was almost nauseating. Joseph pulled off his boots and lay back on his bunk. Suddenly the excitement was over, and now a long, empty time lay before him. He was not sleepy. He guessed that it was not much after eight o'clock. He let himself wonder for a moment what his mother was thinking. Then he got up and put his boots on and went back out on deck.

Joseph walked out to the rail and watched the river, felt the boat shift with the flow. That was more what he wanted. He told himself that in time he would have a better job, and someday he would be a pilot. He would have to accept what he had for now. It would take a few years— but the thought of years, the thought of the bunk room and the stench, and of men like Parkinson to work with, was almost too much to face. A fleeting thought of running for home at that moment passed through his mind, but he could not possibly do that. It would give Matthew too much satisfaction.

Joseph watched the water for a long time, but eventually he went back to his bunk. He lay there all night, sleepless. The men came back two or three at a time, every one of them drunk. Some of them spoke another language that Joseph thought might be German. Joseph pretended to be asleep, but he watched the men through slightly opened eyes. He heard one of the men say, "Where'd they git that skinny boy?" No one answered. Within minutes the men were sleeping, and in a few minutes more, three or four of them were snorting like old hogs. Not long after

111

that Joseph felt a sting on his leg. He slapped at it, but soon there were more, and Joseph realized there were bedbugs. There was nothing to do but lie there and wait for the bites; he could not even hope to sleep. And as if the bugs were not enough, he also heard mosquitoes in the room, buzzing past his ear and finally stinging him on his face and neck. The night was awesomely long. It was five-thirty, not four, when he was finally rousted out, but Joseph had been ready to get up for hours.

Parkinson took Joseph to the engineer and said, "This is your new fireman." The engineer did not move. He was drinking coffee at a table in the crew's cabin. He stared at his plate, which was empty, and now and again he took a big gulp of the coffee, which was black as tar.

Joseph was given a plate of cornbread and a slab of overdone bacon. The cornbread was gritty and only half-cooked. Joseph ate only a little of it, and then he waited for the engineer. Finally the engineer, who was not tall but had a chest like a pork barrel and meaty, round shoulders, looked at Joseph as though he finally realized he was there. "You worked a fire afore?"

"No, sir."

He cursed and spat on the floor. "What are you?"

"What am I?"

"You ever been on the river?"

"Only a little."

He cursed again. He sat for a moment and then added a whole line of vile vows. "Why do they always get me some numb-headed idiot who never seen a furnace afore? Would you tell me that? What kind of little boy they dug up this time?"

"I can work, sir."

"What *are* you?" Joseph did not try to answer this time. "Where'd you learn that talk?"

"I grew up in the East."

"Grew up? What do you mean, grew up? You ain't growed yet. Well, I'll tell you this much, you can't do the job and that's all I got to say."

112

"Mr. Parkinson gave me the job and—"

"Parkinson." He spoke the name like a curse. "That jackass. I shoulda knowed." He sat again and stared at his plate. Two other men came in and sat down at the other table in the room. They looked more asleep than awake. They spoke in the language Joseph had heard the night before, but they said little, mostly just pushed bacon and cornbread into their mouths without any apparent dissatisfaction.

After a period of seeming paralysis, the engineer looked up again. He pulled a pouch from his pocket, opened it, and pulled out a huge gob of loose chewing tobacco. This he plunged into his mouth, dropping a third of it on his shirt in the process. He worked the tobacco around for a while and eventually collected it into one cheek, which bulged so greatly that the whole side of his head seemed distorted. "Awright," he mumbled. "I'll give you one day—'cause I ain't got no one else. But I'll run you off tonight if I can find me a real fireman."

"You'll see I can do it, sir."

"Don't call me 'sir.' Call me Jack. I ain't got no last name, no first names, no sirs, and no misters. I'm just Jack. Now you come with me. You better look lively this whole day or I'll pitch you in the river."

He took Joseph to the furnace and showed him his job. It seemed remarkably simple to Joseph. All he had to do was take the split wood that the deckhands brought to him and feed it into the furnace.

"You'll be he'ping with other things at night and in the morning—if you last that long—but for now just worry about keeping that fire going—and hot—once we get going. Thar's tricks to it. I'll show you what I can when I get the time. Right now just start shoveling out all them ashes. Lucky for you, I cleaned out the boiler last night." He handed Joseph a shovel.

"Where should I throw the ashes, Jack?" The name sounded almost like a "sir" on Joseph's tongue.

Jack swore and spat on the floor. "Whar do you think?"

113

Joseph tried to decide, but he hated to be wrong. "I guess I don't know, Jack."

"In the river." The words thundered from deep within Jack's big chest, and Joseph suddenly felt stupid. It was rather obvious. Joseph went to work. He worked with more intensity than he ever had for Matthew. He had soon cleared out almost all the ashes. Jack came back before long. "Ain't you done?" he growled.

"Just about."

"That's good enough. Come into the engine room with me. We need to grease the pistons afore we start the fire. Cap'n says we're leaving at eight or he'll know the reason why." Jack seemed to be calming down—or maybe waking up—and he seemed a little less grumpy than he had before.

They did the lubricating in the filthiest, greasiest hole that Joseph had ever seen. They were both bespattered with grease themselves before they were finished. Jack grabbed up the stuff in his hands and stroked the huge pistons rapidly, splashing everywhere. After that they returned to the furnace and Jack began to instruct Joseph on lighting the fire and keeping it hot. "Now listen, boy. You keep 'er stoked. Stoke 'er till you drop, 'cause if you don't I'll drop you anyhow. You can't let 'er die down into a bed of ashes. Ram that poker like a devil in hell. You understand that?"

"Yes, sir . . . or I mean, Jack."

Captain Miller came by at that point. "Who's the boy, Jack?"

"Don't know his name. Parkinson picked 'im up. The jackass."

"What's your name, boy?" the captain asked. He was dressed like Parkinson, but he was a shorter man with a well-trimmed beard and reddened eyes. He looked unhealthy to Joseph; his skin was the color of old paper.

"Joseph Williams."

The captain laughed, showing his blackened teeth. Jack laughed too, much to Joseph's surprise.

"Joseph Williams, is it?" the captain said. "Well, boy,

around here you'll be just plain old Joe. Where'd Parkinson pick you up?"

"I came here to the landing and asked for the job."

"Did you run off from home?"

"No. But I left home."

"Can he work, Jack?"

"Not much," Jack answered. "I told 'im he better show something today or I'd run him off tonight."

"Well, we need a fireman, Jack. This don't look like much of one, but we better make him do if we can, at least till we get to St. Louis. It's hard finding a man who's tended fire up on these upper landings, so make him last if you can."

"Well, that's all fine to say, cap'n. But I ain't keeping no wet-behind-the ears boy what can't work. I'd ruther run 'im off and tend fire and do my work both. If he cain't learn—and learn quick—I'd ruther just throw 'im in the river and find out wuther he can learn to swim."

The captain laughed again, his chest rattling as though he were about to cough. "Well, at least he won't get drunk and cause troubles for us. He's too little to drink. Do you drink, Joe?"

"Not much," Joseph said.

They both laughed. "Joseph Williams," the captain said. "Maybe that's Joseph Williams, Esquire. We got us a fine gentleman for a fireman. This here's a elegant old boat, ain't it?" He laughed again, which set off a fit of coughing, but when he stopped he asked Joseph, "Joe, you have anything 'sides those farming clothes?"

"No, sir."

"'Sir,' he says. I like that, Jack. You all oughta show me that kind of respect."

"I told 'im not to be calling me that. I just want 'Jack.' And he gets 'Joe.' So we're straight if he can work like the devil hisself. I don't need no gentlemen working for me."

"Well, you just try your best to keep him till St. Louis, Jack. I'm tired of you raging and running off firemen and then complaining 'cause we cain't find no more."

"I think you'll find that I can do the work, captain," Joseph said.

Both the men laughed hard. The captain slapped Jack on the shoulder and mumbled something about a gentleman, and then he began to cough as he walked away.

Chapter 14

In the next few days Joseph learned why the fireman's job was difficult. The feeding of the fire itself was simple enough, but to keep the fire hot, almost constant stoking was necessary. Much of the wood brought on was not well seasoned. Oak was best for burning, but at the wood yards along the river the captain had to buy what he could get, and that usually meant cottonwood. It was soft and did not burn well unless it was stoked often. Joseph used a long stoker, but he still had to stand directly in front of the fire and catch the full blast of the heat. It became overwhelming. The intense heat of the summer had still not arrived, but the humidity, especially on the river, was high.

The combination of the dampness and the terrific heat of the fire sapped Joseph's strength. The only drinking water was drawn from the river, and it was so full of mud that Joseph's teeth constantly felt gritty. He hated the filthy water, but he consumed it in great quantities because the constant sweating dehydrated him. But the water soon made him sick. Twice, on the second day, he vomited over the rail and then went back to tending the fire immediately.

Joseph's days began at around five. He had to clean out the furnace and then help with the maintenance of the engine. Some days he had to clean the boilers. When the boat put in at wood yards, Joseph was expected to help the deck hands carry on wood. These men had comparatively little to do most of the day, but they had to work frantically when the fueling stops were made. If more than a quarter hour went by on one of these stops the captain would cuss everyone in sight.

The deckhands were powerful men, and comparatively rested; nonetheless, Joseph was expected to keep up with them, pack as much wood and make as many trips. And then he had to hurry back to his fire and get it stoked and hot for immediate departure. Some days twenty cords of wood were carried on and burned.

The boat usually ran until sundown, which in June, of course, was very late. This meant fourteen hours of running most days. And then there was cleaning and repairing to take care of after running hours. When Joseph finally fell on his bunk at night he slept immediately. He knew nothing of bedbugs or mosquitoes—at least not until he felt their work the next morning. Suddenly, after what seemed minutes from the time he had gone to bed, Jack would roust him out and another day would begin.

Part of what bothered Joseph was that so long as the engine was chugging along all right and Joseph did his job, Jack had little to do. He drank a good deal, and he would often lie down and sleep for two hours or more in the afternoons. In fact, no one seemed to be very intense about his work so long as things went along normally. There were some slaves on board who slept in separate quarters from the other hands and who worked much harder than the rest, but they were the exception.

It was true, as the hands told him, that when the boat got on a sandbar the deck men earned their keep. The cargo had to be unloaded and dragropes hauled out, and the men pulled the boat across the bar. But Joseph assumed that he would have to help with that as well. And since the water was still high that June, there was little chance of it happening for now.

After four days Joseph wished he had never seen a riverboat. There was no time to gaze at the water, no feeling of power, no excitement. It was nothing but overpowering work. He rarely saw the fancy cabin passengers who stayed on the upper decks all day. And the deck passengers, whom he bumped against when he occasionally got out on the main deck, were poor immigrants, trappers, and farmers. They were no special pleasure to meet.

Joseph wanted to escape what he was doing somehow, but he absolutely would not quit. He had too much to prove: to Jack, to Ollie, to Matthew, to himself. Maybe someday he would be up in the pilot house, and then it would all be different. But that seemed too far off in the distance to be much consolation.

Joseph hardly ever saw Ollie, and when they did see each other they only nodded, scarcely acknowledging that they were acquainted. But Joseph knew that Ollie was keeping track of him, and so he never wanted to be caught letting down.

On the fifth day Jack said that they should be in St. Louis by afternoon. "Keep 'er running hot so we can get us an evening off."

"I could do much better if we could get a little more oak today," Joseph said.

Jack cursed and spat. "Yeah, and we could all git there fast if'n we could walk on the water. Quit yer belly-aching and just stoke that ol' cottonwood. You're just lucky we been running down the river with the current. I'll tell you right now you ain't good enough to make it back up. The cap'n will prob'ly run you off in St. Louis—if I don't before he does."

Joseph heard a chuckle coming from behind him. It was Parkinson. He had stopped by occasionally to drop a few insults, but he had not been around much. "He's green as green, ain't he, Jack? Look how he wraps up that ol' stoker in rags and wets 'em down. Remember ol' Mike who used to stand right in there close and grab that ol' iron with his bare hands? That's when you're a man, when you git your hands hardened down like that, boy."

"Well, you're the jackass what hired him, Parkinson. Remember that."

"Better'n you doing both jobs, ain't it?"

"Not much. I have to watch him all the time."

119

Joseph had been holding on, controlling himself, trying not to even pay any attention, but suddenly he had taken enough. "That's a lie, Jack, and you know it. You sleep half the afternoon away, and you drink the rest. You haven't helped me once, and I've kept a good hot fire all the way."

Jack stood looking at Joseph quietly, seemingly unaffected. "Clear out, Parkinson," he said, still looking at Joseph. Parkinson left. And then Joseph saw Jack's big bare shoulder roll and saw the fist coming too late. Joseph ducked and caught the blow on his forehead. He saw a flash in his head and then felt himself hit the deck on his back. For a few seconds he saw a strange pattern of lights that revolved slowly, distantly, and all was very calm. But in a moment he could see again. He opened his eyes to see the hot end of the stoker just inches from his face. Jack said, very calmly, "If you want this pushed through your skull or through your gut, just say one word more like that—now, or anytime. When we get to St. Louis today, you git, and don't ever show yourself around the *Roebuck* again. You understand that?"

"Yes," Joseph said softly, all the spark gone from him.

"That's good. Now get up here and start stoking this here fire before I change my mind. If I decide to take your life, I can just do it and then drop you in the river, and no one will ever know any difference. You got lots to learn about the river, Joe."

The point of the stoker, red-orange and smoking, was pulled away from Joseph's head, and Joseph got up. His mind was still not clear; he felt dizzy. Jack handed him the stoker. "Now, boy, you make that fire hot, and when we get to St. Louis that's the last I ever want to see of you."

Joseph said nothing. He stoked the fire. On one point he was in complete agreement with Jack: he also wanted to get to St. Louis as fast as possible. At noon Joseph hurried to the crew cabin and gulped down his cornbread and beans and then got back to his fire. At two o'clock when he went out to the main deck he heard someone say that St.

Louis was just ahead. In the distance he saw the docks stretching along the banks of the river, and he saw the riverboats by the dozens, some of them four times the size of the *Roebuck*. On the hills beyond the docks was St. Louis. Joseph had been there, but almost five years before, and the city had grown and so had he.

Bells started clanging, and Jack went to work in the engine room. The pilot was bringing in the boat to dock— or maybe it was Ollie in command. Joseph wondered. Was Ollie up in the pilot house controlling everything while Joseph tended the miserable fire down below? Joseph was resentful. Everyone seemed to work less than he did and yet no one caught so many insults. But it didn't matter now; in a few minutes they would dock, and then it wouldn't be long before he was off the *Roebuck* and free.

While the passengers were getting off and the cargo was being carried to the dock, Joseph assisted Jack. The boiler room was steaming hot and Jack was hostile. When all was shut down, Joseph expected to be given some further chores, but Jack turned to him and said, "All right now, *git*. Tell Parkinson you want what's coming to you and then clear out. If I ever see you again, I just might break your head for the joy of it."

Jack's bare shoulders, hairy and massive, hunched forward as he leaned over and spat at Joseph's feet. But this was nothing new; the whole engine room was slick with Jack's saliva. The main deck was covered the same way, and so were the crew room and the bunk room. Joseph was relieved just to be getting away from such a place. He said nothing to Jack, but he left immediately. He went to his bunk and got his extra clothes and then found Parkinson on the deck. He hated to have to deal with the man, to tell him that Jack had fired him. "I need to be paid," was all Joseph said.

"You'll get paid with the rest," Parkinson said. "Help finish up with the unloading. You ain't got but about six bits coming anyhow."

"Jack told me to pick up my pay now and to clear out."

Parkinson laughed with apparent pleasure. "He did, did he? Ol' Jack." But the captain had just come down the stairs to the main deck. "Cap'n, you won't guess what. Ol' Jack has run off Joe here. He told 'im to pick up his pay and get out."

The captain turned and looked at Joseph. He did not laugh. Suddenly he turned toward the engine room door and bellowed. "Jack! Jack, get out here." He waited a few seconds and then yelled again. "Jack, get out here on deck this instant."

Jack soon appeared, wiping oil from his hands on an old rag that was already black with grease. "I heard you the first time," he said, and then he spat on the deck and looked at Captain Miller with obvious defiance.

"Then you should've come when I called." Joseph could only see the side of the captain's face, but the vein beneath his ear was swollen, and his neck was splotched with red. "Did you tell Joe to clear out?"

"Sure did."

"I won't have it, Jack. You've run off every fireman on the river. The good ones won't work for us, and you won't give the new ones time to learn the job. This boy Joe is the best we've had in weeks. He worked good and he didn't keep a bad fire. And he don't drink or fight or bother nobody. I ain't about to let him go."

Jack tried to spit, but most of the dark saliva hung on his chin and dribbled down his fleshy chest. "He called me a liar and said I was lazy. I ain't taking that from no half-growed suckling pig like that. He ain't working for me no more."

"Well, at least he knew what he was talking about. You wouldn't know the truth if you sat down on it—and you do more sitting down than anything else. I suspect he wouldn't have called you nothing if you hadn't brought him to it. I'm keeping Joe, and I'm letting you go, Jack. I can get me twelve engineers better'n you here in St. Louis inside a hour."

Jack nodded his head up and down, but his fists dou-

122

bled and his shoulders rolled forward. He was like a great bull. "That's just fine, cap'n. I been thinking about looking for a better boat and a better cap'n anyhow. Just one thing. If I was you, I wouldn't go walking around this town at night too much. You could meet with a accident and end up in the bottom of this here river getting chewed on by mudcats."

"Don't threaten me, Jack. I'll blow your brains out if you come near me, and I won't bother to tote you down to the river. Everyone in town would know that you fin'ly got what was coming to you."

"Just watch your step from now on," Jack said. "And Joe, you'll see me again. That's a promise."

When Jack was gone, the captain turned to Joseph. He grinned and showed his ugly teeth. "Now Joe, I'm going to keep you, like I said. And I don't doubt you called Jack right, and I guess he prob'ly pushed you to it. But if I can find me a engineer tonight or tomorrow, don't call him no liar or nothing like that. 'Cause we got to be on our way again the next morning. Next time something like this happens I'd have to run off my fireman and keep my engineer—you understand that?" Joseph nodded. Captain Miller was still grinning. "One more thing. If you go into town tonight, I'd go along with some of the big hands what could help you. Or better yet, just stay right here. But don't get caught out on some dark street alone. Jack's been known to get real mean with folks over something like this."

Joseph took the advice, or at least accepted the wisdom of it, but he was confused. He had been happy to be getting off the *Roebuck*. Now he almost had to stay. That meant sticking with his job tending the fire. He stood by the rail and looked over at the people along the docks. He was actually in St. Louis, just as he had often wished to be. And yet he was too tired to enjoy it, and he had been warned that he might be attacked should he venture into town. Joseph decided he might as well rest. He had wanted the chance to sleep for days. He went to his bunk and, without bothering to undress, lay down. Ignoring the heat and the smell, he sank into a deep sleep.

At about eleven o'clock Joseph woke up. It took him a moment to orient himself. He was not being rousted out. It was not morning. Then he remembered that he had gone to sleep in the afternoon. One of the deckhands was snoring, but when Joseph looked, he could see that no one else was in the cabin. Joseph knew that the others were all in St. Louis, in the taverns.

Joseph got up and put his boots on, then walked out on the deck. No one seemed to be around. The air was still and warm, with a light breeze blowing, and Joseph felt a sense of strength and well-being that he had not felt since he had left home. He realized that he had passed his first test, that he had begun to prove himself. Maybe he could stick with the fire for a while and then look for a better job. With Jack gone, things would be somewhat better—they had to be. If he could continue to prove himself, maybe he could move up the way Ollie had.

Matthew and Mother existed in some other time now, and he could even think of them without pain. They had their lives and he had his. He would go see them someday, but only after he had piloted his own craft into Liberty Landing.

Joseph walked to the bow of the boat and looked out across the Mississippi. The moon was coming up, just a yellow slice that gave off no light; it was a dark night. The river looked black. Joseph heard voices, some laughter, along the docks, and he saw scattered lamp-lit windows over in the town. It was exciting now to think that he was in a real city and that he would have the day off tomorrow.

Then he heard someone coming down the deck, someone breathing in grunts. Joseph assumed it was a deckhand coming back to the boat, but wondered why he was coming forward to the bow. Joseph turned around and looked into the dark, but he could see only a dark form. Then he saw the shape of the heavy round shoulders and knew it was Jack.

124

"I thought I seen you up here, boy. I guess you knowed I'd keep my promise." He slowed, but kept coming forward. Joseph could gradually see a clearer silhouette, and then he realized that Jack had the stoker extended in front of him, aimed directly at Joseph. "For what you called me and for what you done to me, I'm paying back." His voice was thick; Joseph knew he was drunk. Joseph thought perhaps he could move fast enough to get away. But as he stepped to his left, the stoker flashed toward him, catching his shirt and ripping it open, tearing at the skin along his ribs. He jumped back, but the shirt caught and threw him off stride. He stumbled and fell. He looked up to see the massive shadow moving toward him. And then above the shadow something moved and Joseph heard a terrible hollow thud. Jack grunted and then dropped, smacking the deck with his heavy shoulder.

In a moment another shadow dropped from the deck above. "Joseph, did he get you?"

"Ollie?"

"Yeah. You all right?"

"I think I'm cut some, but not deep. Mostly he just ripped off skin."

"You're lucky. He was trying to rip off more'n that."

"What did you hit him with?"

"A big old wooden mallet. I hit him good, too, with both hands. I mighta broke his head."

"Ollie, you didn't kill him, did you?"

"I doubt it. His head's too hard."

"He almost had me, didn't he."

Ollie helped Joseph up to his feet. "Yup, he did. I thought he did get you, in fact. Let's go in and see how bad it is."

Just then Jack moaned and rolled on his side. Ollie reached down and grabbed the stoker. "All right, Jack," he said. "Now I've got the stoker, and I'll use it if I have to. Now you clear out."

It was a few minutes before Jack could get to his feet, but when he did he left without saying a word.

Chapter 15

Joseph was not hurt badly. Ollie wrapped the wound with a clean rag. Joseph was reminded of the day in Jackson County when Ollie had helped Matthew. Ollie was like a guardian angel, it seemed, sent again at just the right moment. Joseph was rather touched by Ollie's protecting care, but Ollie passed it off as a lucky accident that he had been left on board that night to watch the boat.

Joseph knew how his family would have felt about what happened. They would have called Ollie's intervention a blessing and they would have knelt and given thanks to God. Joseph's impulse was to do the same at first, but he did not. He was not going to start wondering all over again what part God played in his life. That kind of thinking had only led him to confusion and further questions. When he had been a Mormon he had struggled with all that, but now he was a river man.

The next day Joseph and Ollie took a look at St. Louis. Ollie showed Joseph the taverns and dance halls because Joseph wanted to see them, but he just let him look and then took him right back out. Joseph might have protested the day before, but now there was a new sense within him that Ollie had a right to look after him. They walked together through the streets, saw the hotels and stores and blacksmith shops, and walked along the river front where new riverboats were being constructed, bigger than ever. Boats were docked everywhere, every one white with black smokestacks and each with a sign across the front bearing some name printed in black. "Floating palaces," they had come to be called, and the new ones were gleaming and fitted up like hotels. But Joseph knew how quickly they became dirty and bespattered with tobacco spit. He looked at the boats differently from the way he had seen them at Liberty Landing. His love was tempered by experience, even if only a short experience. All the same, he was part of it now, and he felt a pride in belonging. When he saw boys milling about, looking at the boats, Joseph swaggered just a little and hoped the boys recognized that he was a river man.

When Joseph and Ollie came back to the *Roebuck,* the captain was on board. He introduced Joseph to a rather plump, soft-spoken man named Oscar. Oscar was Norwegian and spoke broken English, sometimes difficult to understand. This was the new engineer, and Joseph was happy with the change.

After Oscar and the captain left, Ollie and Joseph climbed to the wheelhouse so Joseph could have a look at it. Joseph stood at the wheel and imagined himself taking over. "I guess you'll like Oscar better for a engineer to work with," Ollie said.

"Yes, I'm sure I will," Joseph said. "He won't yell so much, I suspect."

"That still don't make tending a fire no good job. I know that 'cause I done it for 'bout a year."

Joseph was impressed, almost incredulous. "A year? How did you hold out that long, Ollie?"

"I don't know. I just done it. Just took one day at a time, I guess. I didn't have nothing else."

"But didn't it wear you out?"

"Sure it did. But I learned some things that helped some. You will too. It gets easier after you've done it for a time. If you stoke right you don't have to stoke so much. You'll get it as you go. And don't put in too much wood at once. A hot fire cools if it gets crowded."

"That's right, Ollie. I already found that out. And I also found out that you better get off at the wood yards and cuss the man until he admits he's got some oak. Captain Miller never does that; he just sits back and takes what comes. But I found out you better get up there and tell the roustabouts to grab all of the oak they can, or they'll just grab whatever is closest."

"That's right, Joseph. That's river thinking. You learn quick."

"Quick enough to be a cub pilot before long, I hope."

Ollie looked at Joseph seriously. "It might happen, I 'spose."

"You still think I ought to go home, don't you."

"If I had a good home like you, I'd go there. I know that."

Joseph had no answer for that. He gazed out over the river and let the idea sink in. And the next day Ollie's words floated in and out of Joseph's consciousness all day. He was no longer swaggering along the docks of St. Louis. He was back to tending the furnace and feeling the intensity of the heat again. He wondered whether it was better to hoe for Matthew or stoke a furnace for Captain Miller. It all seemed too much the same to decide.

But Joseph did find the going a little easier now. He hardly saw Oscar, who did his job and merely expected Joseph to do the same. He did not call him Joe, but Joseph— or rather "Yoseph"—but that was all right. Joseph improved his techniques. He found that it was not effective to merely rattle the stoker around and break down the logs that were burning. He began to clear the bedding carefully so that the air passed easily over the piled-up logs. He found too that if he seemed to know his business and wouldn't take no for an answer, oak would sometimes show up in wood yards where the owner had at first said he had none.

Joseph was gradually finding enough time to get away from the fire once in a while and look around a bit. He could step out to the rail for some air and watch the passengers, or watch the countryside. Some boys came and talked to him one day; they said they wanted to be river men when they grew up. Joseph told them it was no easy life they had in mind. He glanced around to make sure that none of the hands heard him; they never would have stopped teasing him.

On the second day out from St. Louis he saw some people on board who appeared to be Mormons. The men were dressed in frock coats and they had families with them. There was a serious, wholesome quality about them that he associated with his own people. He went back to his work, but he was bothered by their intrusion into his new life. As he feared, later that day he heard one of the deckhands mention the Mormon passengers. He hoped that Parkinson would not reveal that Joseph was a Mormon himself.

At noon Joseph left his fire and hurried in to get his beans and cornbread. The food was always the same, but Joseph ate it ravenously, always feeling starved after sweating before the fire all morning. Some of the hands had taken their food out on the deck and were sitting on boxes of cargo. It was cooler out there and so Joseph did the same. Joseph was taking a good deal of teasing from the men by now, but he laughed at it and sometimes returned it, and the men liked him.

Today when he sat down on a box near three of the Irish deckhands, one of them said, "Here's the luckiest boy on the *Roebuck*."

"Lucky? Why am I lucky, Tug?" Joseph knew he was taking the bait, but he didn't mind.

"It's so hot where you work the mosquitoes are all kilt off—that's why. The rest of us get eaten alive every morning and again every evening. And these mosquitoes are as big as chicken hawks this year."

"They do their eating on me at night," Joseph said.

"Ah, but that's where you're lucky again, you see. You sleep way back in the corner far from any flow of air. The stink back there is so great that no mosquito with any self-respect would ever make the trip back there."

"I guess the ones that drink my blood have no self-respect, Tug."

The old fellow grasped his suspenders and laughed, and his friends laughed with him. One of the other men, the one whom everyone called Art, said, "And did you see those Mormon fellers slapping away last night when the mosquitoes were dining on them? I heard one say, 'How can a man live in this country? These devils could carry off a yearling calf.' "

The men laughed again, but Joseph ducked his head and ate his beans. "Yes, they're odd folks, these Mormons," Tug said. "They look as sweet as a field of clover, but you know, from what I hear, every one of 'em takes a solemn vow to kill any man, woman, or child that Joe Smith tells 'em to kill. In Jackson County, upriver, some tell that the Mormons killed babies and little children without so much as an 'excuse me.' "

Joseph kept eating, but he found that his own pulse, along his neck and in his forehead, was pounding. Another man—George was his name—said, "I've heard such things myself. And from what people tell me now, it's all starting again on the north side of the river, there by Liberty. The Mormons will steal a cow or a hog and say it's God's work and glory, and not give it another thought. Folks in those parts are wondering why they ever let them in. A man I talked to said there'd be war before summer ends, sure as anything."

"Well, you can't blame the decent folks up there," Tug said. "I wouldn't want to live by them. I'd be worried for my family. I guess they're worse for carrying off yearling calves than a Missouri mosquito." The men had another good laugh.

Joseph finished his food. He would say nothing. He did not have to defend the Mormons. There was no need to mix his present life with his old one. "But I don't understand," Tug said, "how such nice folks get mixed up in such madness. These that are going on to Liberty now—and I've talked to many before these—wouldn't seem dangerous enough to hurt a soul."

"As I hear it," George said, "once they're in, they don't

dare try to back out. If they do, they are tracked down and done away with. They say that Joseph Smith is a big man, powerful as a steam engine, and he himself has kilt his share."

Joseph looked up at George, who had settled back and was smoking his pipe with a know-it-all manner. Suddenly Joseph couldn't contain himself. "That's a lie," he said. All three of the men looked surprised. "He's strong, but he's kind. And he's never killed a man in his life. Lots of Mormons left Jackson County, and some have left from Clay too, and nothing happens to them. And the Mormons never killed any babies. Why do you men just believe anything you hear without finding out if it's true?" Joseph felt his blood flowing to his face and ears. He had tried to speak calmly, but his voice had shown his anger.

"And how does our fireboy know so much as all that about Joe Smith?" asked Tug. He was laughing, trying to break through Joseph's obvious seriousness.

"I came from Clay County," Joseph said. "Lots of people like the Mormons up there. Ask Colonel Allen at the landing. You can't believe everything some big talker says on the river—especially those that have never even been to Liberty."

"And have you met Joe Smith yourself, since you say he is such a nice feller?"

"I've seen him."

"Is it true he's near seven feet tall?"

"Not at all. He's close to six maybe, and he has big shoulders and strong arms, but he's no giant. I saw him throw a rock one time. He tried to throw it across the Missouri. But the rock only made it halfway, less than that."

Tug laughed again. "So the Prophet throws rocks, does he? And he thinks he can throw 'em across the Missouri?"

Joseph had said more than he should and he knew it. "No. He was just trying to show me that he *couldn't* do it. He was showing me he was only a man."

This the Irishmen found especially funny, and they

131

roared with laughter. Joseph's embarrassment was now greater than his rage, but he was still angry with the men. How could he ever make them understand?

"So you like Joe Smith and the Mormons, do you?" Art wanted to know. "Didn't they steal any of your yearling calves?"

"They're not thieves. I never knew one to steal anything. And they take no vow to kill, either. They're good people, and they try to help each other. They want to build a beautiful city where everyone will be happy and well-off, and where . . ." Joseph couldn't finish.

The Irishmen were all looking at Joseph intently, curiously.

"Tell me, Joe," Tug said. "Is that what your father thinks of 'em?"

"My father is dead," Joseph said. "But that's what he thought of them too." Joseph felt that he was in danger of crying, and he did not want to do that, not in front of three deckhands.

Tug leaned forward and spoke in a sort of grandfatherly voice. "Joe, it doesn't take much to put all this together and figure out who you are. You're one of the Mormons yourself now, aren't you?"

"Not exactly."

"Not exactly? Now how can that be? Either you are or you aren't." Joseph looked into Tug's old eyes, which were creased like an old leather pouch, almost worn out. Joseph felt more truth in what Tug was saying than had probably been intended. "What are you, Joe?"

"I don't know," Joseph said. And then he got down from his box and said, "I've got to get back to my fire."

Joseph went back to work, but all week long as the old riverboat struggled up the Missouri, he was haunted by the conversation. He found himself thinking about the city that Joseph Smith had described, and he remembered his father telling Mother that he wanted his children to be raised in Zion. "What are you, Joe?" he kept hearing Tug ask. Joseph did not want to answer the question. He had

132

come to the river so he wouldn't have to think about such things.

It took a week to make Liberty Landing, and it was late in the evening of the seventh day when the boat docked. After all the work was finished and most of the men were either in town or in their bunks, Joseph stood on the deck near the rail and looked at the dim outline of the bluffs to the northeast of the landing. Matthew and Mother, Ruth and Samuel, were less than three miles away. The rest of the Colesville Saints were just a few miles beyond. Joseph pictured the cabins, saw his own house in his mind. He knew his family would be asleep, but he wondered what they thought of his absence. He allowed himself to think about Ruth and about little Samuel toddling about the house. They wouldn't understand why their brother was gone. And he wondered about Mother and how she was handling everything, whether she had been thrown back into a state of mourning. Was Matthew able to handle all the work? Joseph knew he hadn't been fair in that regard. And Joseph thought about the whitewashed church and the Saints gathering on the Sabbath. He had never really enjoyed the sermons, but he thought of the Knights and Pecks, and the others, with fondness.

It seemed to Joseph that he had been gone not two weeks, but two years, two decades. He wanted to go home. He hated his job, but it was not that. He hated the boat, the smell of it, the heat, the food, the dirty bunk, the sameness—but it was not that either. He was fourteen and he wanted to go home—that was all.

He could walk away from the boat and not come back. It would be easy. No one would miss him except Ollie, and Ollie would say it was the right thing. Four or five times Joseph almost took the first step. But he couldn't do it. As soon as he was ready to start out he would think of begging Matthew to let him come back; he couldn't do that. Matthew had said never to come home. Joseph had made his decision; he felt it was too late now to change it. He thought of going back to his bunk, but the idea was so re-

133

pulsive to him that he stayed on deck, finally trying to sleep on some bags of corn. He knew he would be sorry in a few hours for not sleeping more; the boat was departing first thing in the morning and heading back down the river.

But Joseph didn't sleep much. He kept wondering what it was he had wanted and what had happened to it. He had wanted to travel, to see things, and he had wanted to be in control of a riverboat. But his life had turned out to be only as wide as the river. The river had the power, and the boat was almost nothing by comparison. And the pilot was even less. Joseph had not admitted this much to himself before, and the truth of it stabbed into his consciousness with force and pain. He would have to make the best of it, that was all. That was all anyone ever did in life, he supposed.

Joseph finally slept some. In the morning, when he was cleaning out the furnace, Ollie came down to see him. "Joseph," he said, "why don't you go home? Now's a good chance."

"Who would tend this fire?"

"We can get a fireman. Don't worry about that."

"I can't, Ollie. I won't go beg Matthew."

"You won't have to. Your ma will be happy to see you and so will Matthew. They won't say nothing about all that. Just head out right now, and I'll see what I can do about finding a fireman."

Joseph heard a voice behind them and turned to see the captain. "Don't be telling my fireman to be running off. What's got into you, Ollie?"

Ollie seemed a little embarrassed. "I just think he'd be better off, cap'n. He has a good family and farm here."

"Is that right, Joe?"

"Yes, sir."

"Do you want to go? If you do, say now. I'll have to start asking about for a fireman right this minute. They ain't easy to find this far up the river."

"No," Joseph said. "I'm staying on."

"Good. Then let's get on with the work."

"Captain?"

"What is it, Joe?" He had to stop and come back.

"What are my chances of learning a pilot's work some time?"

"You want to be a pilot?"

"Yes, sir."

"They might not be too bad, Joe. You're smart and you work good. And the owner says he wants to build some more boats, add some more runs. Maybe after a month or two of tending fire, we could start you cubbing, if all goes well. Ollie is not far from ready for his own boat, and we'll need a cub right here on the *Roebuck.*"

That didn't sound bad to Joseph. He could last a month or two, he supposed. "That's good, captain. I'll work hard and show you I can do it."

"Good then. Now let's get shoveling them ashes. We want to leave by eight."

The captain left, but Ollie stayed. Joseph grabbed his shovel and was ready to start to work again, but Ollie said, "Listen, Joseph, he ain't telling you the truth. He mainly wants you to stay. I was told for two years I'd get my chance. I put in a year of fire tending and another one as a deckhand—and then I was lucky to get my chance. It was allus another month or two. And I'll tell you this, too, I ain't about to get no boat for myself this year, nor prob'ly next year neither."

"Well, I'm staying, Ollie. Maybe he's lying and maybe he's not, but I still want to be a pilot."

"Joseph, why? It ain't no wonderful job, like you think it is."

"I know that."

"You know it? Then why do you want it?"

"Because I'm a river man, and it's the best job on the river. You're the one who told me that."

"Joseph, you ain't no river man."

"Yes, I am, Ollie. Right now, that's the only thing I'm sure of."

Chapter 16

Tending the fire was no easier that morning. Joseph had to feed the logs into the hot flames as always, and he sweat as much as ever. And the terrific pounding of the engine was just as dulling to his senses. But Joseph felt a certain sense of victory. He had come away from Liberty Landing and he had not run for home. The next time would be easier. He would concentrate on what the captain had said about becoming a pilot, and he would hope Ollie was wrong.

At noon, however, Joseph heard something that jarred him. When he went to the crew cabin to get his dinner, the Irishmen were eating at one of the tables. "Ah, Joe," George said. "I been wanting to talk to you. Did you hear about your good friends the Mormons?"

"No."

"In Liberty it was all the talk last night. The Clay County folks—the ones you say so dearly love the Mormons—they met last week. They decided the Mormons will have to leave. They told 'em to get out peacefully, or be driven out by force. I guess the Mormons knew they were whipped, and from what everyone tells, they agreed to leave."

"Are you sure about that, George?" Joseph tried not to sound too anxiously interested.

"Yes, I'm sure. It's what everyone said."

"Where are they going?"

"People say that they haven't decided yet. They are looking for land farther north. Most folks hope they leave Missouri altogether."

Art said, "Maybe they just want to get a bit farther

136

back from the river where the mosquitoes won't carry off their yearling calves."

This was a good joke to the Irishmen, but Tug broke through the laughter and said, "Joe, shouldn't you be moving on with them?" Joseph didn't answer. He sat down to eat his beans, but his breath was coming in gulps that were hard to swallow. What would he do if he went back to Liberty Landing and didn't have at least the thought that he could go home if he wanted to? What was Matthew suffering now? All his work was for nothing. Mother would lose her house again. He wondered whether they could hold up under it all. He knew, too, that part of the pain in leaving would be in not knowing where Joseph was—in leaving the house where Joseph would be most likely to return. One thing he had always known was that every day his mother was watching for him, hoping he would come back.

Joseph walked out to the rail and looked back up the river. The bluffs here were much like those near Liberty. He tried to see beyond the wide bend in the river to the west. But then he spun around. "I can't do this," he said aloud. "I won't look back." He went to his furnace and stoked it. He tried to think only of the fire and the job at hand.

Before an hour had gone by Joseph heard the pilot's bell clanging for a slowdown. The engineer released a valve and the pressure blew off in a gush. This usually meant that the pilot had spotted some problem ahead, a snag or a high sandbar. Joseph went out to have a look; he noticed passengers and deckhands crowding to the port side of the boat, along the rail. Some were pointing down the river. Joseph saw a riverboat, maybe half a mile ahead, lying in against the northern bank, half-sunk. As the *Roebuck* neared, Joseph heard one of the black deckhands say, "It's a boiler 'splosion. Look, she's half blowed up."

It was true. The boat was facing upriver, but now Joseph could see that the rear deck area and upper cabins were blown away. The passengers quieted as the *Roebuck*

137

drifted in closer. Then bells began to clang and Joseph ran into the engine room to help Oscar. The pilot brought the boat close and the deckhands dropped anchor. When Joseph came back out on the deck he heard a man yell from the other boat, "Can you take some of these folks on? Some wants to turn back for St. Louis."

"Sure thing," Captain Miller yelled back. "How many killed?"

"We're not quite sure yet. Least 'leven. Some got blowed in the water and so we don't have a sure count. And some's dying still. Do you have any morphine?"

"No, we don't. Would some whiskey help?"

"Not much. Can you hear 'em screaming? We give 'em lots of whiskey already."

Joseph could hear the moans, and he heard a baby crying. The passengers who were not hurt were crowded forward on the boat, which was lying with the bow high and leaning over away from the bank. One woman was holding another woman, her arms around her shoulders. Joseph could hear one of them sobbing aloud and saying, "Martha, what'll I do? Whatever will I do?"

The words went through Joseph. He did not want to think about them. But the captain was yelling, "You hands down there. Get a plank across. Go over and help bring back the ones that's hurt and wants to go back downriver."

Joseph was near the place where the deckhands placed the plank across. As he stepped back and watched them clamber over to the other boat, the captain yelled, "Joe, go on with 'em and give 'em a hand."

Joseph came very close to saying that he wouldn't, or that he couldn't, but then he went ahead and crossed the plank. He went to the large main cabin where the other hands had gone. Though the room was very fancy with wallpaper and glass chandeliers, on the floor were twenty people or more, their moans and sobs filling the cabin. "Help me," a man was screaming. "Please, help me. Oh, it burns, it burns."

Joseph stopped and looked around. All was confusion

138

and he was not certain what he was expected to do. And then he looked down at a man who was lying near the door. He was flat on his back, absolutely still. Joseph was stunned by the man's face. His cheeks had been scalded away so that only a thin sort of membrane covered his cheekbones and teeth. His eyelids were gone; there were only pockets of gray-blue flesh where his eyes had been. His hair was gone, and his ears and most of his nose. It was like the face of a skeleton, except for the thin layer of melted flesh that clung to the bones.

A man kneeling nearby looked up at Joseph. "He fin'ly died just about a minute or two before you come in. He lived like that for however long it's been. I guess it's been two hours."

The man Joseph had heard before was still pleading. "Oh, please, God, let me die. It burns. Let me die. I want to die. Don't make me live like this. I can't take the burning no more."

A woman by him was saying, "Don't talk that way, Harold. Please don't. You'll be fine."

The man lashed out with his arm, knocking the woman away. "What do you know?" he screamed at her. "What do you know? Won't nobody kill me and put me out of this? Please. Somebody shoot me. Please."

Joseph got out of the cabin and off the boat. He went to the other side of the *Roebuck* and stood by the rail for a moment. And then he vomited into the river. He held the rail and took deep breaths for a time, then vomited again. Behind him, he could hear the talk; most people seemed more excited than bothered. Joseph tried to block it out. He looked at the water, watched the steady flow of the river.

"What'sa matter, boy?" he heard a voice say, and he knew it was Parkinson's. "You been puking in the river, feeding your beans to the mudcats? You shouldn't ought to do that; you'll be hungry afore the day's over." Joseph didn't look back. He watched a log that was drifting down the river, moving at an even pace. "I'll bet you never seen

139

nothing like that before, did you? Just remember, it can happen any ol' day right here on this ol' boat. And if it ever blowed, you'd get it straight on. You'd never even suffer one bit." The log rolled as it was caught by a shifting current, and then it drifted away at a different angle. "Still wanta be a river man, Joe? Are you scared?"

"Leave me alone, Parkinson. No, I'm not scared."

"Joe, you call me *Mr.* Parkinson. Remember that. You're so scared you're white." He chuckled with pleasure.

Joseph spun around. "Don't you care about anything, Parkinson? Don't you care about those people? What's the matter with you?"

"Now look, boy, don't you talk smart to me, because—"

"Well, don't you care about them?" Joseph sounded a little less angry, more interested in actually hearing an answer.

"Look, Joe. I don't know none of them folks. They took the same chance I did by coming on the river. I can't spend my time worrying about all the folks dying in the world. Some dies ever' day, and one time it will be me, and ain't nobody going to cry at my funeral."

"What's life for, then? What do you live for, Parkinson?" Joseph was immediately sorry that he had asked. Parkinson was no one to talk to about such things.

"Don't ask me, Joe. That's not my worry. My worry is to get this ol' boat up and down the river, and that's yours, too. Worrying about what life's for is just adding one more trouble to the load you already gotta carry."

"So do you just run from it all your life?"

"Who's running? I'm riding on this boat." Parkinson laughed and walked away, then turned back and said, "Joe, there's more beans cooking if you're hungry now."

Joseph had to see Ollie. He found him in the wheelhouse, left alone there while the pilot had gone down to confer with the captain. "Ollie," Joseph said, as he walked through the door, "I need to talk to you. Did you see those people, the ones that got burned so bad?"

"They wasn't burned, they was scalded by the steam.

140

That's what happens when a boiler blows. The ones forward is all right, but the rest gets it bad."

"I saw a man with his face . . ." Joseph could not find the words to finish.

"I know. I seen three or four like that. I went over there and helped some folks come back."

"One man kept screaming for someone to shoot him. I think he really wanted someone to do it, too."

"I'm sure he did, Joseph. There's things worse than dying."

Joseph had heard the same words many times, but this time they seemed like new words, a whole new observation, and the truth of them sunk into him and filled him up for the moment. For Joseph it was not the whole answer, but it was the beginning of one.

"You all right, Joseph?"

Joseph didn't answer at first; at last he said, "It made me sick. I had to . . ."

"I know. It made me sick too—and scared. But then I'd prob'ly be all right if it happened on the *Roebuck*. You'd be the one that would get it."

"What does it mean, Ollie?"

"Mean?"

"Why do things like this happen?"

"They just blow sometimes, that's all."

"But I mean, why do things like this—you know—*have* to happen?"

"Joseph, you're the religious one. I've tried to understand it all, but I just don't."

Joseph walked to the side of the wheelhouse that overlooked the river. He watched the river for a while and tried to think. "Ollie, I never can seem to get used to the idea that my father had to die. I asked God to let Father live, but he died anyway. I need to understand why it had to happen."

"You can't find out from me, Joseph. I'm the last feller to ask about something like that. You'll have to ask some of your own people."

141

"I did, Ollie, but they all just said we don't know the reasons for everything. Even Joseph Smith told me that."

Ollie and Joseph stood in the pilot house on either side of the big wheel and looked across the river, away from the damaged boat. "Joseph, on the river sometimes you feel like there's a sandbar or a snag ahead, but you cain't see it and you don't know why you think so. Ol' pilots say till you start feeling 'em though, you'll never pilot nothing. Sometimes I get some of them feelings but I us'ly don't trust 'em. I guess that's why I ain't ready for piloting yet. Do you understand, kind of, what I'm trying to get at?"

"I don't know, Ollie. I don't think so."

"Well, that's all the thinking I've done, and that's all I can give you. I guess it'd be nice to know more things for sure, or maybe it wouldn't—I don't know. But the fact is, you don't know many things for sure, so you got to learn to put some stock in the things that just seem right. And then, too, I've seen ol' pilots miscalcalate and make durn fools of theirselves. There just ain't any sure way I know of. At least none I ever heard about. But then, I'm the last one to ask, like I said."

Joseph watched the river and tried to consider what he had heard. "What should I do, Ollie?"

"We'll be here quite a time yet. That means we ain't getting very far today. If you leave in the morning you can be home before the day is gone. If they have to, they can make a deckhand a fireman for a day or two. It's been done before."

Joseph didn't look at Ollie. He watched the river. He tried to get an answer.

Ollie allowed Joseph plenty of time, and then he asked, "You want to do that, Joseph?"

"Yes."

"All right. That's good. I hope I see you somewheres again sometime. But I'll sure feel a whole lot better to get you off this boat."

The next morning Joseph told Ollie goodbye before he left. The captain paid Joseph, but he was angry, and he

142

cussed and coughed and told Joseph it was a filthy trick to run off at a time like that. Parkinson told Joseph that he knew he "never shoulda hired no Mormon boy for a fireman."

Chapter 17

Joseph followed the road along the north side of the river. He got an early start. By noon he was guessing that he was halfway to Liberty Landing. All morning he had been thinking. In fact, he had done more thinking—at least about things that really mattered—than he had in the entire time he had been gone from home.

Joseph was coming over a hill when he saw a man approaching in the distance, riding on a mule. This was only the third person he had seen all day, and so he was pleased. The man could perhaps tell him how far it was to Liberty. He watched the man and the mule move steadily toward him, and then he thought he recognized who it was. It was Matthew. Joseph stopped and looked again. Matthew looked up from under his old black felt hat. He seemed to start—seemed to recognize Joseph—but he came steadily forward without hastening the mule. Joseph was not sure how to behave. From the distance he could catch no sign of emotion on his brother's face. But finally they reached each other and Matthew slid down from Sally's back. "Joseph," he said, "I'm so glad to find you." He took Joseph by the shoulders and pulled him close and hugged him. Joseph clung to his brother. He didn't want to step back and let Matthew see his eyes.

"Were you coming home, Joseph?"

"Yes."

They stepped back, and Joseph could see that Matthew was struggling not to cry. They didn't say anything, but they looked at each other steadily. "I was coming to try to find you," Matthew finally said. "Colonel Allen sent a boy over last night to say you had been there. I told the colonel to let me know if your boat ever came in. But he wasn't at the dock yesterday, and I didn't know until last night you had been there. I figured if I set out today, maybe I could catch up with you at one of the landings. I was going to go all day and night if I had to."

"I thought you didn't want me back, Matthew."

"I know you did, Joseph. I said things that I never should have said. I was too worried about trying to fill Father's shoes. But you were coming back. Why didn't you come that night when you were right there at the landing?"

"I don't know. I almost did, and then I just couldn't. But some things happened on the river yesterday that changed my mind."

"What happened?"

"I don't think I want to talk about it yet, Matthew. I saw a riverboat that had its boiler explode."

"But why did you decide to come back?"

"I don't know exactly. I just decided I belonged with you and Mother and not on the river. I want to come home and do my share. Is it true that we have to leave again?"

"I'm afraid so."

"How's Mother taking that?"

"Right now she's a whole lot more worried about you. She's had a hard time because of it, Joseph, and so have I. We've prayed every day that you would come back to us. And Ruth has cried for you. I really thought you would be back the next day, and so I was stubborn and wouldn't go after you."

"I'm sorry, Matthew. I never should have run out on you with all the work there was to do."

"Don't worry about it now. Maybe it's best anyway, Joseph. You might have been longing for the river all your life if you hadn't given it a try. Maybe this has been good for you. And besides, I managed all right."

Joseph nodded. It sounded right. "I've learned to work harder, Matthew. I can work fourteen or fifteen hours and go to bed and then go right back at it the next morning. Maybe I can make up for some of the work I missed."

"You sound like you've been gone for a year instead of two weeks."

"I think I have been, Matthew."

The boys rode double on the way back, except that they walked the last part because Sally was tiring out. They reached home late in the afternoon. Joseph told Matthew he would like to go in alone at first. When he reached the door he stopped and looked in. Mother was standing with her back turned, by the fireplace. Ruth was sitting on the floor nearby, rocking her doll in her arms. She didn't notice Joseph.

"Mother." He stepped through the door.

Mother started and then turned quickly. "Joseph," she said. Ruth jumped up and ran to Joseph, grabbing him around the waist. Joseph picked her up and hugged her.

"Joseph, are you home to stay?" Mother asked. She seemed hesitant, standing back. "Did Matthew bring you back?"

"I'm here to stay," Joseph said, and he set Ruth down. "I was on my way home when Matthew found me." Mother walked to her bed and sat down. She put her hands over her face and wept. Joseph felt strangely self-conscious. His clothes had been ruined by the grease and dirt and by sparks from the fire. "Mother, I am sorry for all the—"

"Never mind, Joseph. You're home. And before anything else, there are things I want to say to you, things I should have said a long time ago." She sat for a time, still covering her face, gathering her thoughts, perhaps. Samuel came in from the back room and stared at Joseph wonderingly. "Zhozuff," he said. Joseph picked him up and held him in his arms. Finally Mother looked up. "I was wrong to tell you that you killed your father, Joseph. It was the ugliest thing I ever did in my life. I hope you can forgive me some day. But even worse was that I never could bring

146

myself to tell you I was sorry. I still felt it for a long time, Joseph, and I couldn't bring myself to say I didn't."

"But did I kill him, Mother? Do you still think so?"

Mother stood up. She stepped toward Joseph and touched him on the arm. "No, Joseph, you didn't. You shouldn't have said to him what you did—at least not when you said it. He needed us to believe in him right then. But you made a mistake, the same as I did. And I am older and should have had more wisdom."

"I talked to him about it once, Mother."

"I know you did, Joseph. He told me. And I think the matter was settled between you. It was just that he felt you were right, and it was a great sorrow to him. But that didn't kill him either, Joseph. I just wanted something or someone to blame. He was just too weak, Joseph. He fought the best he could, but the fight was gone out of him from all the sickness. It was his time to die, and that's what we have to accept."

"But Mother, how do we know . . . I mean, we prayed for him to live, and we had the elders and the bishop bless him. Why did he have to . . ."

"Joseph, I don't know. But I have quit asking. The Lord has given us Matthew to get us through. Matthew's a blessing to us, Joseph. And now the Lord has sent you back. We'll be all right."

"But what about losing the house again?"

"I've resolved that too, Joseph. When I thought I had lost you in Jackson County I promised the Lord I would be stronger if you and Matthew would just be brought back safely. Then when I lost your father I thought God had betrayed me, and I gave in to my weakness. But I've prayed for you again, Joseph. And now I have you. I'll never cry about a house again. You and Matthew can build us another one." Joseph nodded, too full to say anything. "But Joseph—look at me." She stood firm as Matthew, or even Father. "I want you to show your strength."

"I will, Mother," Joseph said. He fought back tears for

a moment, and then he said, "But Mother, I still don't have everything straight in my mind. I thought about things all morning."

"For right now, could you try to trust in your father? Could you try to keep your commitments to him? You at least knew to come home; now can't you just trust for a time and maybe you will know more for sure later? You're still very young, Joseph."

"That's about what I decided, Mother. Mostly I plan to work like I never have before to make you another place, and a place for Ruth and Samuel."

Joseph set Samuel down and looked at his mother, waiting. They looked at each other until tears were running down Mother's face and Joseph could barely see for the tears in his own eyes. Finally she pulled him to her. He felt the wonderful softness that he had missed for so long.

It was a hot summer, but there were good rains and the corn did well. Joseph walked alongside Matthew and felt a sense of purpose in the task at hand. When the harvest was in, the boys stored some of the corn and told Colonel Allen they would be back to get it before winter. They sold the rest.

The Saints had promised to leave after the harvest was in. Alexander Doniphan and some of the other influential citizens of Clay County had helped arrange for a new county to be created in the northern part of Missouri along Shoal Creek. The Mormon leaders had agreed to settle there with the unofficial understanding that they would not be bothered so long as they stayed to themselves. Few old settlers lived in the area; it would be a place where the Mormons could build their own city however they pleased, where no one would bother them. And it was good land. Old settlers didn't want it because it was mostly prairie, but the Saints understood how to break the heavy prairie sod, knew what good farms could be made on the prairie. The Saints were more or less satisfied with the compromise, even if it meant starting all over again.

On the last Sunday before most of the Colesville Saints planned to leave for their new settlement, church services were held in the whitewashed church. Newel Knight gave a fine sermon. As he was about to close he paused for a time and carefully surveyed the little congregation, then said, "Brothers and sisters, we have suffered more in the last few years than we ever thought we could; we have all lost loved ones. There is no way to measure the depth of pain and disappointment we have lived with. But on the other hand, look at us. Look what we are. We are stronger than we ever were. Our faith has been tried and we are stronger, not weaker. I hope too that we have learned by both the good and the bad examples we have seen around us. We need to leave this place with a deepened spirit of Christianity, with a deeper sensitivity to all those who suffer. We need to thank God that we have been granted the chance to suffer and thereby learn and gain strength."

It was a strange doctrine; it almost made Joseph smile. What would the men on the river think of giving thanks to God for the troubles that came to them? But the contrast also struck Joseph in another way. He thought of Parkinson and compared him to Newel Knight. It was as though he saw Brother Knight for the first time. The man had lost his wife and his child and had spent a Missouri winter in a shed. He had given up all that he had possessed in New York—a good house and a business—and now he had returned from Ohio with his new wife and was ready to start again. And he was thanking God for it all. It was a curious way to look at things, but Joseph felt a wave of warmth and rightness in it all.

After the meeting Joseph took the long way home. He walked down to his spot by the Missouri, and sat and watched the water, spotted driftwood. Joseph wondered what Father would think of this new place called Caldwell County where the Saints would try to build their city one more time. Maybe Father's dream would happen yet.

Before Joseph left, he found a good stone and threw it with all his might. It traveled well out into the current, plopped into the water, and disappeared. Joseph still wished that he could make a throw that would arch out as wide as the river, but he let the thought go, and went back to his family.

A few days later all was loaded and the house was boarded up. Colonel Allen had allowed the improvement on his land as payment for Sally, and he had sold Matthew another mule. Matthew had harnessed up the team. He and Mother sat on the seat of the wagon with Ruth between them and Samuel on Mother's lap. Joseph sat on the back of the wagon and watched the cow, which had been tied to the wagon with a halter rope.

Matthew clucked at the mules, and the wagon creaked and started to roll. All over Clay County the Saints were moving out. The Williamses were to meet some of the other Colesville people near Liberty and then they would travel together. It would take only a few days to make it to Caldwell County.

When the wagon had gone only a little way, Matthew reined up the mules. Joseph looked around to see what was happening. "Joseph," Matthew said, "do you suppose you could find a place to sit where you are looking straight ahead, the way the rest of us are?"

Joseph understood. He had to fold his legs under him, but he turned around. "All right, Matthew," he said, "I'm turned."

"All right then," Matthew said, "let's all agree. As we ride away, no one looks back at the house or at the river. Are we all agreed?"

They agreed. The little wagon rolled on toward the bluffs and no one looked back.